The *The* BIG FALL

Living with Hair Loss

by

Sheila Jacobs

Published by:

NEW CENTURY BOOKS
P. O. Box 43093,
4739 Willingdon Avenue,
Burnaby, British Columbia,
V5G 4S2, Canada

Graphics by Sheila Jacobs and Tom Benjamin
Computer layout by Tom Benjamin

Canadian Cataloguing in Publication Data
Jacobs, Sheila, 1955-
The Big Fall

Includes bibliographical references
ISBN 0-9694734-1-9

1. Baldness—Popular works. I. Title.
RL155.J33 1992   616.5'46   C92-091788-7

To Tom for his unfailing patience, love and enthusiasm, to Janet for her splendid work and to all the alopecians who have helped and inspired me over the years.

Contents

ACKNOWLEDGEMENTS

I would like to thank the many people who have generously contributed their time, expertise and interest to this project, particularly Dr. Jerry Shapiro and Pat Jacobs for their medical knowledge. Many readers helped shape The Big Fall, including Liz Dohan and Glenda Christie from the British Columbia Cancer Agency, Dr. Sue Mackie, Lorraine McCulloch, Ray Taylor and Greta Jacobs.

Thanks to Lindy Barrow and Jeannette Christie for their archives, to David Noble at the British Columbia Cancer Agency library and to Vicki Kalabokes of the National Alopecia Areata Foundation. I also appreciate the responses from Wendy Thompson, Rick Smith and all the other alopecians who contributed their experiences.

Lafern Page joined me in a productive experiment in writing and feedback, which was invaluable for this book. I would like to thank Claire Kujundzic for her insights and work on the specific issues facing creative workers, and Nick Bantock for colouring outside the lines.

Finally I am deeply grateful to my patient editor, Rhoda Kaellis, to Eugene Kaellis and to Tom Benjamin who has lived with this project for two years and plunged into the adventure.

INTRODUCTION

This book is about hair loss and its effect on people, sufferers and non-sufferers alike. Whatever the cause, everyone it strikes shares psychological trauma. Losing hair is only a minor inconvenience, physically; we can find ways around having less or no hair to keep the head warm in winter, no eyelashes to screen dust and grit. It's looking different from the average person that causes the anguish. A few people are indifferent to hair loss, but the sadness of loss haunts many for a considerable time; the emotional scar remains.

When all my hair fell out through alopecia areata I felt totally isolated, and needed to find out more about this ailment. I wanted more than the medical facts, more than cosmetic information. I wanted enough social and psychological background to put my experience in context. That's one reason why I've written this book - it provides a more complete picture than the books focusing on one aspect of alopecia. I do not, however, discuss wigs or hair transplants at length because developments would soon overtake what was written.

Everyone who loses hair meets someone who says, "What's the problem? It's only hair." But hair is not an 'only.' I decided to find out why losing hair is such a challenge. I wanted to write a book that offers ways to cope with the shock and restore the confidence that vanishes along with the hair. My own hair loss was sudden and unexpected, but

I explore both temporary alopecia in chemotherapy patients and the more gradual loss most men and some women experience as they age.

For many hair loss sufferers how other people react is the biggest anxiety, so I examine this in detail. What's acceptable in hair varies from culture to culture, and through history; part of the book looks at the many meanings hair has, and has had, for us humans.

The people I'm writing for above all are those who have lost hair, so I've tried to use as little medical, psychological and sociological jargon as possible. I hope that those indirectly affected by hair loss - family, friends, fellow-workers, doctors, mental health professionals, nurses, teachers and those in the hair industry - will find this book a valuable and comprehensive guide to this neglected subject. Because hair loss is often a very private concern, I have changed some details in the personal quotations I have used, to maintain confidentiality. The bibliography contains publishing details of works referred to in the chapters.

People with less hair have had a bad press for far too long. It's time to stop being anxious about being called "baldy" and start being proud of being a "silkhead" or "alopecian", a "highbrow" or "chrome dome". It's time to change a stigma into a distinction.

Chapter 1

FROM TEARS TO TELEVISION

THE FALL: BRISTOL, ENGLAND, NOVEMBER 1987

I'm losing a lot of hair. I can't even joke about it, as I often do to cover up some difficult or confusing state I'm in.

It's such a shock that I can't believe it's really happening. Time seems to stand still as in a nightmare. It reminds me of when I had a bicycle accident. It seemed to take forever for my foot to slip into the front wheel and for the tangle of me and bike to tilt and skid all along the road.

Hairs keep dropping yet I compulsively comb out more and more, unable to believe that the fall can continue. I keep thinking,

"This isn't really happening."

Then when I can no longer deny it, I feel I am wading against invisible forces in dreamy detachment:

"This isn't really happening to me."

Panic

My mind cannot face this. It can't be happening, yet it is. Like a child who hides its eyes to shut out something disturbing, by retreating into a safe fantasy world, I am numb, trying to block it out - yet I know there's only a thin layer of cracked ice over hysteria and panic.

November 1987 - My hair fell out completely in just over three weeks. In my diary, before it all vanished, I wrote:

November 16th

I am balding and ancient. I look like Lord Longford with his fluff of fringe around the baldness and wrinkles - only I have fewer jowls and more crackled network. An extra depressed phase this evening - the hair falling out still

This is the first diary entry about losing my hair. The previous pages are starkly empty. I shied away from writing about what was happening, hoping it was a temporary mystery, that this bald desert of my head was a mirage that would vanish - if I ignored it. Ostrich. But by November 16 it was obvious and undeniable. What caused me terrible pain and grief was seeing this so familiar face in the mirror changing from day to day. More horrifying than seeing Dr. Jekyll turn into Mr. Hyde, because it wasn't some actor transformed by the illusion of makeup, but me, in a waking nightmare. Real life. My life.

Having to look in the mirror to arrange my strands was agonizing. My streaked blonde bob just fell apart, day after day. Soon all I had left were patches of thin hair, which I carefully arranged beneath the beret I now wore constantly. I hoped people wouldn't realize that something weird and terrible was happening to me.

Seeing my own despairing, terrified face every time I looked in the mirror reminded me of Oscar Wilde's story *The Portrait of Dorian Gray* - except I felt I'd done nothing to deserve this metamorphosis.

Lack of trust

I couldn't discuss what was happening with anyone, because I was too choked up. I broke down whenever I tried to talk about it with my partner, Tom. 'Talk' is the wrong word. I screamed, cried, ranted, hit the walls, blamed him.

2

Shortly before my hair began to fall we had our first major argument, over a situation in which I felt demeaned and betrayed. For years I had repressed resentment over a particular aspect of our life together, because I didn't want to upset Tom. When at last I voiced my feelings, he ignored me - and all the stored-up rage and pain exploded. To me, our relationship, now complicated by a shared mortgage, seemed doomed. The fact that Tom didn't think we had a problem only proved to me the depth of our incompatibility.

Just when I so badly needed one person to trust enough to express my grief, I was hurt and angry, feeling abandoned and completely alone.

My life was in ruins but I didn't know how to tell anyone. What if they responded with disgust or horror, or faked acceptance? I didn't want to be an object of pity. If I got sympathy I might start crying and never stop. My one wish was to disappear off the face of the earth, never to have contact with anyone, haired or not, ever again.

Shame

I want to wallow in misery at home. But I'm in the midst of a job setting up a computer system for a new art gallery. I work freelance: there's no one who can take over. And I have a mortgage to pay.

Before my hair began falling I felt out of my depth with this project. Now I can barely concentrate on my work because I have to keep sweeping hairs off the keyboard so the gallery owner won't see them. Is it shame? Or anxiety that the owner might realize there is something wrong with me and fire me? I buy a floppy velvet beret before bald patches appear, and wear it all the time. He must realize something weird's happening - but I can't explain. What could I say? I don't know what's happening myself.

Here I sit in his beautiful medieval house, in a beautiful

3

English village, designing a system for his art gallery - and I'm turning into a mutant. I feel disfigured. I want to cry, but I'm too busy watching for the stray give-away hairs.

I did a terrible job for that man.

Anger

Desperate, looking for reassurance, I go to my doctor, who tells me I have alopecia totalis, meaning I will be bald. BALD! She tells me the cause is stress and seems embarrassed by the problem. She refers me to a dermatologist and suggests that meanwhile I get a wig. Her diagnosis, referral and advice are completed in just a few minutes.

I couldn't believe it. I hadn't known people could lose their hair just like that. I enjoyed colourful, bohemian clothes and had been part of an 'alternative' scene since student days. When my doctor suggested I wear a wig I felt she was trying to turn me into a suburban senior at the age of 31. At the time I had no idea what a big cross-section of the world wears wigs to hide hair loss. I was furious with her for suggesting it, furious that it would obviously make her feel more comfortable; deep down, I refused to believe my hair really would disappear completely. I had gone to her expecting medical treatment or a cure, not mere cosmetic advice. Rage struggled with shock and grief. I wanted to cry, but didn't want to walk red-eyed through the crowded waiting room.

I just held it all in.

Horror

As I lost my hair, my face became more noticeable. My eyes seemed to shrink in size and visibility as the defining boundaries of eyebrows and eyelashes just disappeared. My forehead, always high, now appeared to be half my head, big and featureless as a grain silo. In contrast to my reddish face and neck, the skin once protected by my hair was like a white cap. Without the distraction of hair, eyebrows and lashes, I began to pore over my skin. It was blotchy, a legacy of years of eczema. Wrinkles were exposed where my eyebrows used to be. Creases from nose to mouth. And the web of tiny wrinkles that are part of the texture of skin, so you know it's not plastic, leapt into prominence. To my panic-stricken magnifying eyes they looked like ravines all over my face and head. Every time I looked in the mirror I saw my small, frightened, naked eyes looking out of the hideous mask of a stranger. Worse, a stranger who bore some resemblance to the real me, the one with hair.

Hall of Fame

QUEEN ELIZABETH 1st of England had around 80 wigs to choose from to cover her sparse hair. Her fully-haired attendants diplomatically followed suit.

Every time I had to arrange my patchy hair to look more 'normal' or make up my eyes so they didn't look so starkly hairless, was a stab to the heart. Tears often prickled at the back of my eyes. When they overflowed I would have to start the makeup all over again, prolonging the agony. And when I cried, my nose and eyes would swell and redden, my lips go pale, and where my eyebrows once were would turn red and blotchy. My appearance seemed even more appalling.

The worst, the absolute worst, was knowing this was not a nightmare. I wouldn't wake up from it. I was stuck with it. There was nothing I could do in the short-term and maybe nothing at all, ever. I had nobody I could turn to who had been through this. I had no idea how to cope, or what life I could possibly have as a bald woman. Many a time I wished I were dead. Intense and horrible emotions blotted out rational thought. My bald head filled my universe, pushing everything else into insignificance.

There were brief spells when I would forget about the hair loss. I might be out gardening in the chill grey winds of our coastal home, completely absorbed in the rhythm of weeding or digging in compost. And then I would experience the utmost despair as I remembered: my hair was almost gone. Or I might wake from a lovely dream, feeling tranquil and happy about life and the day ahead. Then I would remember. And all joy, tranquillity and energy would vanish as I realized I was in the nightmare of my own life. At our home near Bristol, in England's West Country, I used to watch our pond with its fish and teeming insect life - it always had the power to take my attention off problems and to restore perspective and serenity, almost like meditating. But now any time I tried it, my eyes would flood with tears so I could hardly see. How could the pond go on as normal when my world was falling apart?

Isolation

I'd suffered for 25 years with asthma and eczema, in a problem family background. After years of physical disfigurement my eczema was just starting to clear. How could life be so unfair?

Even so, I was relatively lucky when my hair fell out: I already had a support network. I had joined a co-counselling group - that is, we paired up and counselled each other regularly. I could have all the counselling sessions, training and workshops I wanted. But my hair loss was too painful to deal with, as I discovered at a workshop about getting close to people.

My best friend and a trusted colleague were at the workshop, but couldn't dispel my shame at my baldness. I was convinced that no one would want to get close to me, that I was abnormal, and that my head was something disgusting that I ought to hide from others, even my best friend. Surely even these people in my counselling group, who were committed to seeing the lovable human in everybody, would not be able to accept me as I really was - almost bald. I couldn't accept myself. When you're terrified of rejection, the safest thing to do is shut the door. In tears, I confessed to the group that I didn't want to be close to anyone. Perhaps if they had all been bald, I would have been able to admit that at heart I was longing to feel close, accepted and loved, especially now.

During the lunch break, one man asked to see my head, still hidden under the beret. Tom alone had seen the new me. I refused, feeling angry and threatened. But he was a man I trusted, a helpful official from my old trade union. He continued very quietly, as I cried, to tell me he really wanted to see me without my hat. Finally I pushed up the edge of my beret, revealing all of four square inches of my bald scalp. Waves of shame swamped me, and tears poured out. I couldn't look at him because I expected to see horror and revulsion. But he hugged me and thanked me for being brave enough to show him my head - and the workshop continued.

Fear of Exposure

I was sitting at the very front of the comedy cabaret. The place was packed but a friend, Helen, had saved seats at her table for Tom and me. We had an excellent view of the star, a bizarre gay punk who called himself the Joan Collins Fan Club (his real name was Julian Clary). He was wrapped in black plastic, had a studded collar round his neck, and wore more make-up than Joan herself. (Clary has now shed his plastic and scaled the heights of camp entertainment to become a game show host on British TV.) After running through a gamut of tricks with his patient mongrel, Fanny the Wonder Dog, Julian turned on the audience. First he descended on two women at the table next to ours. They had masses of showy hair, all highlights, perms and extensions. "Ooh," squealed Julian as he snagged his fingers on their sculpted glory, "what *lovely* hair! Did the council do it?"

(In England, town councils have a reputation for substandard service.)

Suddenly he swooped over to our table, grabbed Tom's bag and pulled out his diary. "Massage, it says here, dear," he leered at me, "did you know about that? There's a phone number too" I sat burning with fear. I don't remember anything else he said, any of the comments that had the crowd howling with laughter. All I could think about was that beneath my beret my head was bald except for a few wisps of hair. Several friends of mine were scattered about, but nobody in the whole place except Tom and Helen knew about my hair. Trying to escape would certainly draw Julian's attention to me. The place was hot; panic and embarrassment were making my face even redder and sweatier than before. Couldn't I just faint when he whipped my beret off?

But my worst fear went unrealized. Julian was distracted by a heckler from the shadowy recesses, and moved off to

> ## Hall of Fame
>
> SIGOURNEY WEAVER, film star, shaved her head to appear in *Alien 3*: "I felt it was really contemporary. It made women's hair look kind of old hat."

a new target. That was the night I learned this 'cosmetic problem' was in a very different league from, say, having uneven teeth.

Grief

I began working on my hair loss with my counsellor, Janet. It was the hardest thing I'd ever done. I couldn't stop crying, but sharing my terrible secret with someone else lessened my shame and turmoil. She led me kicking and screaming into areas I didn't want to go, allowing my full anger and despair to surface over the dermatologist's verdict:

"When you lose all hair from your scalp, the prognosis for regrowth is not good. It may come back at any time, but it's possible it may never come back. There's no treatment worth trying with alopecia universalis." The almost-bald dermatologist then dismissed me with: "It's only a cosmetic problem. Now see the receptionist about getting fitted for a wig."

I was furious at the implication that I had wasted a specialist's valuable time with a cosmetic problem. The phrase suggested that losing all your hair is no more significant a problem than having an unsightly pimple. The assumption was that I was making a fuss about nothing. Rage seemed easier to focus on than the bleak, blank despair it concealed.

Janet patiently encouraged me until I took off my beret for her. She encouraged me until I looked at myself in the mirror, completely hairless but with her strong loving arms round me while she gazed at me with appreciation and compassion. Anguish and humiliation swept through my body and I cried so much I wondered if it were possible to damage my sinuses or tear ducts. But I started to 'clear out.'

I found the courage to tell a few close friends. Then to

9

show my head to one or two of them. Slowly I began to recover my sense of identity and my life. I don't remember much about how my immediate family reacted, as I was myself overwhelmed. I am grateful they didn't add to my problems. Later, I discovered that they were stunned. Tom felt *he* had really messed things up, but assumed it wouldn't all fall, or would at least soon grow back. He was desperate to convey that he still loved me. "People's appearance isn't that important to me - I always go for personality, that's what counts." Having contracted a painful illness at the time of my alopecia, he was frustrated at being unable to give me the attention he wanted to.

I phoned my parents long-distance to tell them. They were shocked and sad, but didn't overdramatize; they were more concerned about seeking cures. Both work in medical fields, and perhaps this and the fact that they have endured adversity themselves gave them a sense of perspective. My mother-in-law had suffered temporary hair loss herself some years earlier; when Tom told her mine had gone, she says she was lost for words. My in-laws' polite affection provided continuity for me; I could forget about the whole thing in their company.

There are no other diary entries until Christmas, when I rented a seaside cottage for a week with Tom and friends. What went on? I know from photographs of the holiday that I took my hat off among them while indoors, and out on the deserted cliffs in the sunlight. I was testing my toe in the water. My friend Glynis, an excellent photographer, took pictures of my head because she thought it looked interesting, but I was shocked and dismayed when I saw the results. A photo is so objective compared with a glance in the mirror. This large bald head emerged from the parka like a peculiar fruit. I thought I looked like the bald villain on the *Thunderbirds* puppet shows we'd loved as children.

That photo was a small piece of sadness I buried inside me: with friends' support I was less devastated about my hair loss, but the emotional improvement didn't show on my head. Part of me must have expected that I would soon stop looking so abnormal - or unusual, as I was learning to rephrase it. These illogical hopes kept recurring as the years passed until eventually I was able to look at my head without sadness, surprise or disappointment.

But for now I was agonizingly self-conscious about my appearance. Dammit, I didn't even know what to *call* the new part of my head that had become exposed! Scalp suggested hair. Head meant the whole lot above the neck. Skull was just the bone. Did people in the Middle Ages have a name for the bit they shaved? Whoever uses cranium or pate in conversation these days?

Frustration

I tried to pencil on eyebrows, without success. I'd often gone without makeup, and seldom spent more than five minutes slapping some on, so I was frustrated to tears at my inability to recreate the appearance of eyebrows and lashes. I resented having to wear makeup every day now, instead of spontaneously. I felt I'd lost my freedom to be me.

THUNDERBIRDS VILLAIN THE HOOD

Those first couple of months were a roller coaster of emotions and thoughts on how to combat this peculiar condition. I didn't want to get a wig because it implied

11

accepting that I'd be bald for the rest of my life. If wearing a cotton velvet beret in winter made me hot and sticky, what would a wig be like, especially during the summer? It would be bound to irritate my eczema. And how could I go swimming, or sunbathe? Would I ever have a normal summer again? This was no idle speculation: my beret would be too hot in warm weather. How could I wear a straw boater or a cotton sunhat indoors while doing computer work for clients? I couldn't go bald. And I didn't want a wig. How could my life continue? I examined all these new anxieties in counselling sessions.

THE UNVEILING: CANARY ISLANDS, FEBRUARY 1988

After three months, I was becoming familiar with this totally new appearance. When friends said I looked good without hair, I did my best to believe them and accept that perhaps I wasn't the ugliest thing on earth. Surviving other people seeing my naked head allowed me to move on to talking - purely theoretically, of course - about taking off my hat in public. I wanted a holiday, a break from all the stress of the last three months. So I planned to go to the Canary Islands, a favourite winter sun spot for the British off the Atlantic coast of Africa.

My friend Emma agreed to come with me. When I told her I was planning an experiment - taking my hat off among complete strangers - it didn't put her off the trip. In fact, she was excited to be part of it. I would have died of fright at home, but two thousand miles from anyone I knew, on a relaxing holiday, with a supportive friend seemed the safest way to leap off this cliff. I didn't *want* to do it, all I wanted was hair; but I realized I had to be practical.

We found a cheap hotel room in the small resort of Los Cristianos on the island of Tenerife. The first day I walked about sweating in my beret until I bought a big cotton sunhat and walked around in that. The following day was the test: we would go swimming. We went to a beach that wasn't too crowded, choosing a spot for our bags and towels close to the water. Still wearing the hat, I got into my swimsuit. In spite of the tension that gripped me we were both laughing at the strangeness of it all.

"Ready?" Emma asked.

Do or die. I pulled off the hat, raced into the sea and swam. It really was happening. I was in public and bald! When I waded out of the water I noticed a few people staring. The surprise was that most people weren't, they were going about their business, reading, sunbathing, drinking, talking - not looking at me. I put my hat back on and lay down on my towel. I'd done it, and survived.

What felt like possibly the end of the world was only the beginning. The next day I walked around town bareheaded and got more stares. People were curious, surprised, shocked, but not hostile. Nobody attacked me or yelled or laughed at me, as I'd feared. I wondered if a growing awareness of cancer and chemotherapy had something to do with the tolerant way strangers responded to my baldness. Although I felt like an animal in a zoo, Emma comforted me and made me laugh. Realizing I didn't have to be ashamed was the most liberating experience of my life. I began to think anything might be possible. By the end of the week I was more optimistic than I had been since my hair fell out, and smiled at the thought that I must have given many surprised visitors and locals a holiday to remember.

On our last night, an even more surprising thing happened. In true 'Brits abroad' lager lout style, we had quite a bit to drink over dinner and then went on to a disco. To my amazement men flocked around, bought us champagne, and flirted with us - both of us. I almost fainted! I had been convinced that without hair, no man would ever again look at me as a woman.

I've never been a beauty - I'm 5'2", weigh 135 lbs, take size 14 clothes and have what I kindly class 'sturdy peasant legs'... and now I had no hair. But here were all these men, dying to get to know us. We had a roaring night of champagne and dancing, ending with a moonlit beach stroll. Clearly some men didn't find baldness a turn off at all, in fact they *liked* the way I looked. Even a hideous hangover on the bumpy flight home the next morning couldn't dispel my astonishment and joy at the way the hairfree holiday had turned out.

This springboard launched me on a program of uncovering my head. First among friends, which always led to plenty of questions about this mystery condition, alopecia. Then in a restaurant - I reckoned people in restaurants would be polite and constrained, though I wasn't so sure about pubs.

The first pub I tried was a quiet one, in the safety of a group of friends. Incredibly, nothing terrible happened. It was as if I had gone through a raging shipwreck only to wake up not dead but on a lovely island. Yes, some people stared - but not all of them. I took courage in both hands and began to mention my hair loss at the different places I worked - while still wearing the beret. I encountered no rejection. Eventually as it grew warmer I dared to take off my hat for short periods in the street. Then for longer periods, extending my comfort zone.

This didn't mean that everything was just dandy from then on. Often I'd get home and cry, whether I'd endured many stares or not. Sometimes I got angry at being gawked at as if I were a circus freak. Adjusting continued to be a long and bumpy process.

During this period I tried many approaches to regrow hair: acupuncture, homeopathy, art therapy and autogenic training. (Like hypnosis, this latter included relaxing and visualizing my hair regrowing.) In 1988 my hair partially regrew, only to fall out completely a couple of months later. Learning to live with baldness, having my hopes raised, then smashed once more, was very, very, difficult. I realized there would be no easy way out of this. Still I hoped my hair would grow back so I would not feel so vulnerable and different all the time.

It was hard work to believe Tom when he assured me he still loved me. When my hair first fell I couldn't believe that any man, even my partner, could find a bald woman sexually attractive. My desire had vanished along with the hair, but my experience on Tenerife acted as a kind of reality check, and I started to feel more attractive, and more sexual.

I'M NOT ALONE: BRISTOL, 1989

I returned to work as an employee for the county council where I had worked three years before. My new post was in the Equal Opportunities Unit, where disability was a primary issue. Mixing with the hundreds of employees I used to work with caused me apprehension. Some were rather conservative and I dreaded their shock or disapproval over my strange new appearance. My heart sank at the prospect of having to explain what had happened. But once more, reality smiled at my fears. I explained my condition to my new colleagues and to the small group I had worked with before, and hoped word would spread. I decided to act as if I looked like any other worker; I was

15

rewarded with people treating me as a normal human being.

Thanks to my supportive boss and colleagues, I hardly thought about hair loss at work. Occasionally other employees would mention my condition with deep sympathy and ask in hushed tones if there were any news of a cure yet. I had grown accustomed to my looks and no longer felt as if I was in the midst of tragedy; their kind but heavy-handed response hinted they viewed it differently. It jarred a little, but revealed how much things had changed for me in just one year.

In fact, now that I felt better about myself, how others reacted was of great interest to me. I had became interested in behaviour and psychology while doing developmental group work with young unemployed adults some years earlier. Now I felt like David Attenborough observing the curious antics of hairy creatures in the world around me.

IF YOU DON'T GO TO SLEEP AT ONCE, THE **BALD TURISTA INGLESA** WILL TAKE YOU AWAY!!

There were those who pretended they hadn't seen me, or hadn't noticed that I was bald. This seemed a particularly British and Canadian form of politeness. Some simply stared. This frequently happened when I was on holiday in more emotionally open countries such as Turkey and Spain.

A few were curious enough to ask me about it outright; often they had a relative who had lost hair, and such conversation provided a bond I appreciated. There were some who suggested I wear a wig, and some who couldn't look at me when they spoke. Others couldn't take their eyes off my shining pate; it's strange to find people talking to your forehead rather than your face.And a phenomenon I had noticed first in the Canaries was that when they caught sight of me, older men often unconsciously stroked their hair, as if needing reassurance it hadn't suddenly fallen out in sympathy with mine.

By 1989 I was managing to live a fairly normal life, although I still didn't socialize as much as before, and sometimes felt uncomfortable in public. Tom and I were planning to sell our house and move to Canada, to see more of my mother, who is Canadian, and to experience some open space and relaxed living. In July 1990 we got married, and in September put our house on the market.

The wedding was a small and informal occasion. A designer friend helped us create outfits that included matching pillbox hats - I felt very stylish and comfortable. After a wedding lunch with family we held an evening party for around 30 friends. Once more, it turned out that losing hair didn't have to mean losing out on marriage or fun.

Then to my joy I discovered a network for alopecia sufferers. Others like me really existed. Until I found the Hairline network I hadn't realized what a struggle it is to be one of a kind: no one to share experiences, learn from, no really knowledgeable support. I hunted out the book on hair loss written by the network's founder, journalist Elizabeth Steel, *Coping With Sudden Hair Loss* . I was delighted to have information about alopecia, because unlike cancer or male baldness, little is known and less is written. The book provided practical and medical material, with plenty of case histories: fascinating stuff, since people lost and regained hair in a totally random way, no rhyme or reason at all. But wigs featured prominently. For the first time, I realized how different my experience was from most who lost hair.

My observations of people's reactions, my counselling sessions and ponderings led me to conclude that the main problem with hair loss had to do with what's considered 'normal' - a conclusion many others have reached. Why does a painless physical difference drive people to despair, divorce or even suicide? I reckoned it was because we aren't generally visible. Society can't get used to us because most of us hide it. If all of us threw away our hairpieces tomorrow, we would be seen as the ordinary, numerous minority we are, and people *would* get used to us. In other words, the cosmetic problem of alopecia is actually psycho-social; we're not socially accepted, so feel pushed into leading double lives, which takes a psychological toll.

Fuelled by these ideas I sat down and wrote an article about my experience of alopecia. *The Guardian*, one of Britain's quality daily papers, published the article. When it came out, I nearly died. The photograph they had taken of my bald head was LIFESIZE. It took up more space than the thousand words I'd written. It revived the old feeling of wanting to hide from everyone.

I received several letters from readers. Some were moving accounts of their own experiences of hair loss or of the problems experienced as daughter or parent of a sufferer. Most expressed gratitude that I'd brought the subject out into the open, and that I'd been brave enough to bare my head in public; several wished they dared to do the same. I decided to organize a meeting to talk about the emotional aspects of hair loss rather than medical treatments and cosmetic issues. Ten people came from London, Wales, and southern Britain to Bristol in December 1989 and we spent the day talking about how hair loss affects us. We shared out time equally between us. I was very nervous but my trusted counsellor Janet - with her full head of grey hair - was there to give me support. I handed out a counselling program I had written detailing the steps I had taken to work through the trauma. I felt honoured to meet the other women and men who were in the same boat, navigating uncharted waters.

One of my strangest experiences was meeting Julia, another openly bald woman. When I first saw her through a window I was sure I was seeing my own reflection - until she moved. It was like discovering a long-lost twin, although with hair we must have looked quite different from each other. Finally, after two long years, I met others like me.

Before I moved to Canada the support group met again, and is still in touch today; one of the members is setting up a Positively Bald group in London. Meanwhile other papers and radio stations had noticed my article and phoned me for interviews. I talked to staff at the Bristol Cancer Help Centre about hair loss, and made a short video with one of their doctors. My head had become newsworthy. It was bizarre that what I had spent months trying to hide was a passport to minor fame.

And in February 1990 I was invited to appear on a TV talk show about alopecia areata organized by Elizabeth Steel. She assembled people with widely differing views and experiences, from a senior who had been bald all her life and never told anyone except her husband, to wig makers, doctors and a model who had shaved her hair off and found it useful for work. And so the poor bald scalp I'd initially regarded with horror made it onto national TV.

Doing alopecia work felt wonderful. Here was something I knew lots about! I could look my alopecia square in the eye and say - Okay, now what? Every time I was interviewed or talked with people about it, the wound healed further. It turned out to be a practical way to work through shame and denial. There was so much involved in this issue of hair loss that I decided to write a book about it.

THERE SHOULD BE A BOOK ABOUT IT: CANADA, 1991

Tom and I moved to Vancouver in May 1991. I was born in Canada so I was 'returning home.' I discovered to my surprise I wanted to buy a wig for my new Canadian passport. Airport customs had searched me twice in the last two years, probably thinking that with a haircut like mine I was something dangerous like a drug dealer or a Buddhist monk.

I put off buying the wig till the last moment. During my lunch hour I dashed into a theatrical costumers and was confronted with Morticia wigs or bubbly neon (lilac, orange) swinging sixties perms. Panic! But when I explained what I wanted the assistant led me to a real wig section. I was disappointed that none of them looked particularly good on me, but thought I might as well go for the kind of hair I had always wanted. I chose a thick, gently waving auburn affair with a synthetic shine, shelled out $70, and went off to the photographers. I cringe when I see the photo now: I look like an anxious Dallas extra. It reminds me of my period of hell. The wig is stuck away in a cupboard; I have a new one that suits me for the odd time I want to wear it. In any case, Canada let me in.

One of the first things I discovered when we settled in Vancouver was an alopecia areata support group. What luxury! And there were not one but two North American alopecia networks: the Canadian Alopecia Areata Association, based in Edmonton, Alberta, and the National Alopecia Areata Foundation, based in California. The Canadian network produces a newsletter with poems, stories and lots on the emotional aspects of alopecia, feeling good in spite of hair loss. The American network covers medical research, support and cosmetic issues, and features plenty of letters with readers' experiences. It also organizes support groups from Alaska to New Mexico, and provides excellent information on running a support group. The two organizations complement each other well.

> ## Hall of Fame
>
> **WILLIAM SHAKESPEARE** found that a receding hairline in a playwright of genius is called a high intellectual forehead. "There's no time for a man to recover his hair that grows bald by nature." *(Comedy of Errors)*

Another alopecian, Wendy Thompson, and myself volunteered to lead the Vancouver support group in September 1990: no one else wanted to do it. Running the group has been a valuable experience. At times it has seemed nothing but an added burden; other times I notice just how much I gain from it, as do other members.

In November 1990 I went to the NAAF conference in Atlanta, Georgia. A weekend among 300 others with the same condition was a wonderful, experience. I felt at home for the first time since The Big Fall. I came away wiser and happier, enriched from meeting such a wide cross-section of Americans and Canadians; I benefited from their insights, experiences, and ways of coping.

Before the conference I had been pleased with the way I'd handled my hair loss. I thought I'd dealt with it. But it didn't happen in a vacuum; it lifted the lid from other issues I had avoided for years. Feeling unacceptable, the silencing shame, the desire to avoid other people, echoed much of my life experience.

As a five year-old immigrant with a Canadian accent I was rejected by classmates at my English school. Although outwardly we were a jolly Catholic family, behind closed doors raged endless hostilities. I developed severe asthma and disfiguring eczema. In addition, most of the people at my high school and at Oxford University were from more middle or upper class, moneyed backgrounds - all important in class-conscious Britain. While my friends' brothers were at the top English fee-paying schools, my brothers were serving Borstal sentences for juvenile crime. While my friends and I graduated with honours degrees, two of my brothers graduated to heroin addiction. Remaining unemployed in spite of hundreds of job applications had left me with the impression I was a piece of garbage. Shame, confusion and the despair of the powerless had silenced me all my childhood and adolescence, and hair loss replayed the same terrible emotions.

In my confused teenage years only alcohol had made me forget my misery and helped me feel adequate enough to mix with others. It was alcohol I leaned on when my hair fell out. Processing the new devastation uncovered this complex of older layers: I thought I had reached the top of the hill only to find an Everest towering above me. The shift from devastation and despair to functioning and optimism gave me the confidence to face the chronic issues of dysfunction, co-dependence, alcohol and drug abuse, and the impact of the class system, unemployment and eczema on my self-esteem. Listening to others at the NAAF conference proved I was not the only one affected by these issues; the very fact they talked about such subjects brought tears of relief.

Writing articles about alopecia areata showed me how much there was to explore. A book was in there somewhere. I began to work tentatively on the project - *No Hair? No Sweat*, I called it, though later I came up with the more delicate *Nectarine or Peach*. Only after a hilarious brainstorm with a friend, therapist and writer Lafern Page, did I settle on *The Big Fall*. In the first few months in Canada I wrote rough drafts of the first four chapters. I dreamed of earning a living through the book and freelance writing. But there is little budget for freelance journalism in Vancouver, and no publication like *Venue*, the magazine I'd written for in Bristol. And every publisher I contacted in 1991 and '92 turned down the book because they thought the market was too small. Deciding to fund and publish the book locally gave me another chance to work on that sense of vulnerability, and has given me purpose and a sense of the real, strong, creative me that the hair loss damaged.

Hair loss turns out to be more like a game of snakes and ladders than a problem with a solution. It affects self-esteem, and that affects almost every aspect of life. The only way I have found to cope with it is to remain flexible, vulnerable, and humble - willing to help others, but ready to learn and accept help too, and even ask for it.

The Meaning of Hair 1

Hair is a symbol of sexual, heroic or divine power, and intimately linked to the soul or spirit. It is used as a tribal and religious distinguisher, and often features in rites of passage such as initiations, marriage, and burials.

The Indo-Europeans introduced the ideology of sun worship and male power to the Middle East and Europe during the Bronze and Iron Ages. Their priests and warriors wore streaming hair and beard to symbolize the sun's rays and their power. The vow not to cut hair was taken by the Jewish Nazarene sect, orthodox Jews, Hindu yogis (following their fertility god Shiva), Sikhs, Rastas, and Russian and Greek Orthodox Catholics. Heroes such as the Greek Heracles, biblical Samson and Babylonian Gilgamesh had long hair and beard and accomplished astonishing feats of strength. In legend, the Irish hero Cuchulain and the wild Norse Berserkers displayed a fiery battle-light (halo) round their heads as they charged into war. Biblical prophet Elisha was so touchy about his lack of priestly hair that he cursed a gang of boys who were shouting "Baldy," and God sent bears to kill over forty of them.

Most cultures, from Egyptian to Iroquois have rituals and legends that treat hair as a charm against danger. When lovers exchanged locks of each other's hair it was a sign of commitment and trust. The power of hair could destroy, too, and besides hair being used in magic to harm its owner, there were many taboos to do with when it was safe to cut or comb it. When women loosed their long hair it was believed to unleash storms, as well as kindle men's lust. To avoid this, girls 'put up,' covered or cut their hair upon entering womanhood or marriage.

Chapter 2

FIRST AID FOR FALLOUT

Who It Happens to and How

Everyone knows about hair loss. It happens to men when they get older, though a few younger men get thin or receding hair. Oh yes, and some cancer patients lose their hair.

That's the popular myth. And it's wrong. Anyone can lose their hair, at any age. Women and children are the invisible sufferers, as they almost always wear wigs. And many men cover up with toupees, transplants or weaves. Hair loss must be one of the most common yet best-disguised problems in the world.

On an average scalp there are over 100,000 hairs; the figure varies according to hair colour and ethnic origin. At any time about 10 per cent of the hairs are in the resting (telogen) stage of their growth cycle. Nails are biologically related to hair: both are live at the roots but dead at the ends, and both grow continuously while healthy. In rare cases, nails may also be affected by the cause of hair loss, becoming dry or brittle.

The medical term for any kind of hair loss is *alopecia*, from the Greek word αλωπηξ (alopex), meaning fox. Not because doctors consider people without hair pretty foxy, but because the ancients observed one cause of hair loss is the ringworm fungus, which causes fox-mange. Hair loss can be sudden or gradual and may involve body and facial hair too. Diagnosis can be difficult, since causes vary from fungus to chemotherapy to hormones to - who knows what. With alopecia areata, for example, the medical profession knows some of the factors involved, but hasn't yet discovered the cause.

There are four main types of hair loss: androgenetic alopecia (male pattern baldness, which as female pattern baldness affects women too), drug- or illness-related hair loss (including chemotherapy/radiation), telogen effluvium (hair becomes sparser) and alopecia areata (sudden, inexplicable hair loss).

This chapter only summarizes the medical aspects of hair loss, as the pace of progress means information is constantly changing. For up-to-date medical details, see your doctor or specialist, and contact the foundations or groups listed at the end of this book.

Androgenetic Alopecia

This is by far the most common type of hair loss, accounting for 95 per cent of people who become bald. The usual name, male pattern baldness, is inaccurate as it occurs in women too; some dermatologists call it female pattern baldness in these cases. Its medical name is androgenetic alopecia, because it is related to an increased production of the hormone testosterone, an androgen. Although testosterone is usually thought of as a 'male' hormone, women produce it too, though in smaller quantities. Similarly, men produce 'female' hormones such as oestrogen, again in smaller quantities than women. The hormone change generally occurs with maturity, but some men are affected as early as their twenties. A genetic predisposition to this type of hair loss is also involved.

Thus as people age, around 50 per cent of men and 40 per cent of women are affected; and men on average lose more hair than women, because they produce more testosterone, to which their hair follicles are more sensitive. While 10-20 per cent of women suffer some hair loss before menopause, it is mostly when women are older that thinning becomes more noticeable.

Androgenetic alopecia can develop in various ways: a general thinning in quantity, receding at the temples, or a bald patch on the crown of the head. Over several years these thin or bald areas may spread until a monk's tonsure results - just a fringe of hair round the back of the head is left. With androgenetic hair loss, hair usually disappears only from the scalp: body hair, including eyebrows and moustache or beard are usually intact. Aristotle, writing in the 5th century BC, claimed that eunuchs never become bald - not enough testosterone, presumably.

Androgenetic hair loss is a common stage of sexual maturity; it occurs in some monkeys, too. Most men of European descent develop baldness, given a long enough life, but it's less common in those of African descent and least common in Asian or Native American men.

Hair Loss Through Chemotherapy or Radiation

The best known type of drug-related hair loss is in cancer patients undergoing chemotherapy or radiation treatment. Cancer itself doesn't cause hair to fall out: the drugs or radiation used to treat cancer attack all cells, including healthy hair cells. But when chemotherapy or radiation finishes, hair almost always grows back, though somtimes more slowly than expected. It does not, however, always take the same form as before, with regrowth thicker, or curlier or a different colour. This curious phenomenon can also happen to those with alopecia areata.

People exposed to high doses of radiation, such as those caught in the fall-out from the nuclear accident at Chernobyl, can lose hair too. Whether or not it regrows, and when, depends on the quantity of radiation exposure.

Other Medically-Related Hair Loss

Crohn's disease is another instance where the drugs used to treat the disease cause hair to 'thin,' i.e. fewer hairs grow so the scalp is more visible. Other drugs that may induce hair loss include anticoagulants and any drug that interferes with the body's ability to synthesize cholesterol. Even aspirin and ibuprofen can, very occasionally, cause hair loss. Research into the possibility that vaccinations might in rare circumstances trigger hair loss is under way in Britain.

A few illnesses actually cause hair loss - that is, no drugs are involved. These include cirrhosis (or other malfunction) of the liver, ringworm, disorders of the thyroid gland, syphilis and diabetes. People who have had illnesses with fever, such as scarlet fever or meningitis, sometimes find their hair becomes sparser or falls out entirely. Changes in hormone levels may affect hair too - many women find they lose some hair after childbirth, or if they stop using birth-control pills. Conversely, a surge in oestrogen during pregnancy often results in a visible increase in quantity of hair.

Telogen Effluvium

During its growth cycle the hair enters a 'telogen' or resting phase. When this phase is entered early or is prolonged, the result is fewer hairs on the head, although the follicles remain. This typically leads to a sparse period of weeks or months, after which more hairs resume growth and normal appearance returns. Telogen effluvium is one from of diffuse alopecia (thinning hair) but there are others. Once the cause has been diagnosed, appropriate treatment can be offered. One cause is of telogen effluvium is stress, but the mechanics aren't yet understood. Because many of those whose hair thins don't seek medical help, the per cent of the population affected is unknown.

Alopecia Areata

Alopecia areata is sudden, unexplained hair loss. This kind of alopecia is called *areata* when one or more small round bald patches appear on the scalp, *totalis* if all hair disappears from the scalp but remains on the body, and *universalis* if it vanishes everywhere. (For simplicity, I generally use the term 'alopecia areata' to refer to this whole group, including totalis and universalis.) Around 1 per cent of the population is likely to experience alopecia areata by the age of 50, for some period of their lives. The

> ### Hall of Fame
>
> MARK MURPHY developed alopecia areata at age 8, but went on to play football for the Green Bay Packers for 12 years and promote public awareness of alopecia areata. "The big thing in life is not what you don't have, but what you do have and what you do with it."

small bald patch or patches occasionally spread to form larger, irregular patches, but more commonly they vanish as hair regrows after a few months. Hair usually regrows in such larger areas within a couple of years. But bald patches can recur, in the same or new places.

The tiny subgroup of those with totalis or universalis have a smaller chance of all their hair returning; only 50 per cent of those with universalis get regrowth. People who have developed alopecia once are more likely to develop it again.

It appears the immune system 'attacks' hair follicles to prevent growth, as though the hair is a dangerous foreign body. Why this misunderstanding occurs is not yet known, but there may be a genetic factor. Experts disagree on whether stress is involved.

Other Causes of Hair Loss

Excesses or deficiencies of proteins, vitamins and minerals may also cause hair to fall out, e.g. too much vitamin A or selenium, too little iron, zinc, copper or vitamin B. (This may account for hair loss in those on crash diets.) Diseases that interfere with the digestion of proteins, vitamins and minerals may therefore also harm hair growth.

Finally, hair may fall out through being 'traumatized' by continual pressure. This can happen with hair styles such as pony tails or corn row braiding; through severe treatment at the hairdressers (e.g. perms and bleaching); through regular rubbing (e.g. farm workers' rubber boots may cause bald patches on their legs); or through a nervous habit of pulling at it.

How it Affects Sufferers

The issues that arise when hair falls differ according to the cause. Cancer patients coping with the physical pain and emotional and mental upheaval of cancer - the life and death issues - may find hair loss insignificant in comparison. They know their hair will vanish only temporarily. For some, however, losing hair is the last straw; it assumes importance as the most visible, inescapable sign of the disease. Experiencing one's familiar appearance change drastically can be traumatic. Dr. Joyce Yasko and Patricia Greene comment that many patients have said the temporary hair loss "was the most stressful event they experienced during their illness." (*CA - A Cancer Journal for Clinicians*)

Someone with alopecia areata may suffer depression not only because of the sudden change, but because of the uncertainty over when or even whether hair will regrow.

Since there is no pain or danger to bodily health, they can feel defensive about being considered vain, and suffer from general ignorance about the condition.

The gradual nature of androgenetic hair loss makes it easier to adapt to than the shock of sudden change. But once hair disappears in this manner, it will never return. While many people aren't worried about it, others feel this is the beginning of the end of their life, and that they are on a downward slope in terms of youth and attractiveness. In addition, other people may belittle their emotional pain as oversensitivity or vanity. For men, this smacks of being called unmanly. For women, losing head hair and the frequent labelling of this loss as male pattern baldness can make them feel they are losing their femininity.

What To Do When It Goes - Medically

Only cancer patients know beforehand that their hair is likely to fall out. Nancy Bruning, in the chapter on hair loss in *Coping with Chemotherapy* , suggests asking doctors which drugs affect hair, and to what extent. She also stresses the value of having hair cut as short as possible before treatment begins. Specialists usually advise patients to choose a wig or scarf and start wearing it *before* their hair vanishes. Preparing for a changed appearance makes the transition to being hairless less of a shock. Hair loss will, fortunately, be temporary. Only those with brain tumours or who have needed extremely high doses of radiation might experience scant regrowth or permanent baldness.

People whose hair falls out quickly and unexpectedly, however, usually want to get some sort of covering at the first opportunity - a hairstyle that looks fuller, or a scarf, hat or wig. This makes the sufferer feel less exposed and eases the process of adjustment. If the problem is small bald patches or thinning, a good hairdresser can restyle hair to cover. Most hairdressers have experience with thinning hair, chemotherapy or alopecia areata.

When hair starts to vanish, it is vital to consult a doctor. A non-medical hair clinic or trichologist is no substitute - they are not qualified to diagnose the cause and can't pre-scribe medical treatments. They may cost a lot of money, and in some cases can do more harm than good. If medical treatment doesn't work, these can be tried later.

After carrying out any necessary tests (e.g. for anaemia or thyroid disorder), the doctor should make a referral to a specialist. This is usually a dermatologist, an expert in skin and hair disorders. It often takes weeks to get an appointment to see a dermatologist, depending on the ur-gency of the problem. The sooner the cause of hair loss is diagnosed, the more effectively treatment will work.

> **Hall of Fame**
>
> ASHELY SIEGAL founded the National Alopecia Areata Foundation in 1982, and transformed the lives of thousands. "God created a few perfect heads... and the rest he gave hair to."

Emotional Support

Meanwhile, every budding "silkhead," of whatever category, needs to get support and infor-mation. The worst ap-proach is to do nothing, in the hope that the problem will go away. Confiding in someone is most important - a partner or a close friend or family member. Choose somebody who is sympathetic and a good listener. Those who feel extremely depressed or upset should look for a crisis line listing at the front of the phone directory. Trained counsellors are there to take phone calls in confi-dence. Or a family doctor might be able to recommend an organization skilled at coping with people in crisis.

Contacting a hair loss network will provide information

and may put the alopecian in touch with others with the same problem. Reading their leaflets and newsletters really helps. It reminds people that they're not alone, and aren't 'freaks.' Millions of people survive hair loss but it takes time to adapt.

'Cures'

Recipes to cure baldness are as old as the hills - or the pyramids, at least. The earliest known medical writing - an Egyptian papyrus from 1600 BC, copied from a 3000 BC medical work - recommends a mixture of red lead, arsenic, onion and alabaster. With treatments like this, perhaps nobody got close enough to notice the hair loss.

As soon as my hair started to go I noticed ads for miracle cures everywhere, often at miraculously high expense. Fortunes are still made from peddling the modern equivalent of snake-oil. People suggested I try this or that lotion, electric stimulation, yoga, mantras, all sorts of therapies. Some people may have found that a certain formula works for them. However, any remedy guaranteed and proven to work for everyone would likely have been bought up and marketed by a drug company, since they would stand to make millions. Hair loss is so common there's a big market for 'cures,' and customers are sometimes distressed enough to spend lots of money.

Each individual has to decide whether or not they want to risk trying such cures, how long they will try them for, and how much they are prepared to spend. Buying or trying on impulse, when feeling low or faced by a persuasive salesperson can lead to serious debt, and no extra hair. Take time to do some research: ask to talk to other satisfied customers and contact your hair loss network to see if anyone knows about the product or process.

Trying one treatment after another, medical or alternative, helps some sufferers to cope. A business consultant

33

> Burne the head of a great Ratte and myngle with it the dropping of a Beare or of a hogge and anointe the heed, it heleth the desease called Allopecia

LloydS TREASURY of HEALTH
15 85

with alopecia areata gave her philosophy:

"I'm always trying different things. If I didn't, I'd feel I'd given up. It keeps my hope alive, so I don't drop into depression. I need to feel I'm doing all I can to fight this thing."

Yet a study by Dr. C. Gosselin found that in the case of male pattern baldness, those who tried treatments that were unsuccessful were more depressed than those who didn't try any treatments at all (*Personality and Individual Differences*).

Treatments

Little medical research has gone into hair loss compared with, say, cancer or heart disease. This is understandable, since hair loss is not a killer, nor is it physically painful or disabling. Given budget restraints, it is a lower priority for research funding. Until it happens to you, it is hard to imagine how terrifying and *emotionally* disabling alopecia can be. But research into treatments does continue: drug companies realize the potential gold-mine a cure or successful treatment could be.

Minoxidil - sold as 'Rogaine' in the USA ('Regaine' in Britain) - is a drug originally developed for high blood pressure, with hair regrowth a side effect. It's not the wonder drug researchers first hoped: it works best on androgenetic hair loss, thinning hair and on those with small areas of alopecia areata; and the results do not always match hopes, in terms of quantity of regrowth or percentage of success stories. Like many other treatments, Minoxidil can have side effects and needs to be applied forever after, or the improvement disappears. Because it doesn't treat the actual *cause* of hair loss, it cannot cure it.

Oestrogen lotion sometimes helps thinning hair (whatever the cause) in women. It is not used in male pattern baldness because of side effects such as breast development and loss of facial hair.

Research into alopecia areata is still in the early stages and no cause has yet been discovered, although various leads are being followed. Dermatologists don't know exactly why the condition happens, or why it turns itself off, usually of its own accord.

Studies show alopecia areata occurs slightly more frequently in patients with a personal or family history of auto-immune diseases such as asthma, eczema, vitiligo and lupus. The cause may be a combination of a genetic tendency towards this kind of auto-immune response, or a genetic irregularity in the hair growth cycle, plus something that triggers the immune system to attack the hair follicles. This is similar to what is understood of allergies: in asthma, the body mistakes harmless particles of pollen, say, as dangerous, and overreacts by producing too much histamine, which narrows the space available for air. When hair grows back during treatment it is difficult to judge whether the treatment *caused* this or whether it was about to regrow anyway.

Other medical treatments for alopecia areata are sometimes successful. Generally, the less hair you have lost, and the less time it's been gone, the better the chance for regrowth. The most common treatments include:

- corticosteroid injections into bald patches. Mostly successful, side effects unlikely except around eye area. Oral steroids (in the form of pills) can regrow hair but taking this powerful systemic drug can cause widespread side effects e.g. weight gain, cataracts, diabetes, ulcers, depression and lowered resistance to infection if used over a long period.

- skin irritants and allergens applied to scalp sometimes trigger regrowth, possibly by distracting the immune system away from the follicles to the irritated area. Various agents can be used: dinitrochlorobenzene (DNCB), diphencyprone (DPCP), squaric acid, even the leaves of a species of primula. Treatment is successful in around 50 per cent of cases, but hair often disappears when treatment stops. Drawback: itching rash may affect other parts of the body.

- anthralin, a tar-like ointment is successful in some cases but may irritate or discolour skin.

- PUVA involves treating skin with light-sensitive psoralen, then sensitizing with ultraviolet light. Success rate low, treatment time-consuming. Ultraviolet rays increase risk of skin cancer.

Tourniquets have been used to combat hair loss during chemotherapy but side effects and the reduction in efficacy of therapy makes this controversial. No safe way of stopping hair loss during chemotherapy or radiation has yet been found.

Although surgery is not recommended where regrowth is possible, hair transplants can transform the lives of men with androgenetic hair loss who were depressed about their appearance. One entrepreneur in his thirties declared:

"It's the best investment I ever made. My depression has vanished and I have recovered my old personality.

People don't make cruel comments any more. When most of my hair had disappeared, I felt horribly middle-aged."

The drawbacks are that besides the expense, transplants give less and less adequate cover if hair loss progresses. Maintenance is costly and the scalp becomes progressively more scarred. In addition, every surgical operation is a trauma to the body, stressful on its resources.

Some work has been done on diet, although medical professionals disagree over the role nutrition plays in hair loss. Crash diets have caused hair loss, perhaps because of vitamin or mineral deficiencies. It would be interesting to find out whether vegetarians are less likely to develop androgenetic hair loss than meat-eaters since animals raised for food are often fed androgen-like steroids. Androgens are removed by the liver, which means that anyone who drinks a lot of alcohol or takes drugs that interfere with the liver's functioning might be keeping their androgen level high. Pervan and van Deusen's books (on male baldness) cover this in some detail.

Wigs, hairpieces, toupees or weaves - prostheses as they are called by professionals - are the usual way of dealing with hair loss. Wigs are made from synthetics (cheap) or real hair (expensive), and come in a huge variety of styles, weights, methods of manufacture and ways of affixing to the head. Modern methods include interweaving false hair with the client's remaining hair, although like transplants this requires investment in maintenance. Mixed technology involving both surgery and wigs have a greater margin of error, need continuing aftercare at the clinic, and are therefore expensive. Just as with non-medical treatments, research beforehand is advisable.

Current Research

As hair loss becomes increasingly high profile more medical research is being funded. Some by drug companies such as Upjohn (who make Minoxidil), some by government medical research bodies such as NIAMS in the USA (the National Institute of Arthritis, Musculoskeletal and Skin diseases), and some by the fundraising efforts of support networks such as NAAF. People with alopecia areata sometimes object that mostly preventable illnesses such as heart disease, strokes and lung cancer, grab a large part of the resources, while alopecia remains a Cinderella.

In the last few years researchers have discovered minoxidil and grown hair in a test tube; continuing research in these areas should increase understanding, if not provide more effective treatments. Current research includes electric stimulation of hair follicles, laser combined with sensitization, and research into both normal hair and abnormal hair biochemistry and growth cycles at the cellular level.

YES, THE TEST TUBES NEED A LITTLE FINE-TUNING BEFORE THEY'RE COMPLETELY COSMETICALLY ACCEPTABLE

Because hormones have such a complex and powerful effect on the body, doctors are reluctant to use oestrogen in attempting to restore hair in androgenetic hair loss for men. Whether oestrogen treatment helps androgenetic hair loss in women is debatable. The rate of hair loss often slows after menopause is over.

Few dermatologists completely agree about

what's going on, physically, in alopecia areata. Until recently, the favourite culprit was stress. It's well-known that stress can affect the body's immune system, lowering natural resistance to disease such as colds, pneumonia, arthritis, and cancer. It may be implicated in asthma, eczema and migraine. Some dermatologists, however, reject the stress theory. They point out that people whose hair starts to vanish are indeed stressed - by this very event. These days, most people would confirm they had experienced stress recently. Why doesn't everyone's hair fall out when stress occurs? Why does it only happen to one per cent of us? Most specialists believe there is some additional physical cause such as a genetic irregularity in the hair growth cycle or an immune dysfunction.

Much of the latest research has been at the cellular level of the immune system. Certain 'defence' cells produced by the immune system, helper-T cells, are unusually numerous around the hair follicles in the bald patches. These defence cells attack as if the hair is a foreign body, thus preventing normal growth; very occasionally, they manage to kill the follicle. There have been studies using immune-suppressing drugs such as cyclosporin but this can leave the body defenceless against any disease, which is extremely risky.

Future Trends

The immune system is an 'in' area of research at present - it's central to AIDS, allergies, and alopecia, among others. There is also the newest branch of medicine, psychoneuroimmunology - PNI for short. PNI studies the links between the mind (psyche), nervous system and immune system, as well as the endocrine (hormone) system. As more about these links are understood, our knowledge of all illness and the role of stress should improve enormously.

Some dermatologists believe that alopecia areata could be a collection of diseases that simply share the symptom of hair loss. How much hair falls, how quickly and for what length of time varies so much from person to person that no one can yet account for it.

There will probably be new insights into the effect on health of environmental factors like carbon monoxide emissions from cars and electromagnetic fields near power lines. At present, very little is known about this complex area, and there is uncertainty over whether such factors are involved in cancer and immune-related disorders.

Cancer is a well-funded major research field, where some very dedicated and open-minded professionals are working. As the only cause of hair loss is the treatment, research to target chemotherapy only at the cancerous cells continues; this would mitigate much of the pain and sickness involved in treatment. If people are encouraged to manage stress better and choose healthy diets and lifestyles, if concerted action is taken over carcinogens such as tobacco and nuclear waste, cancer should become rarer in future decades. Today a minority of cancer patients choose alternative approaches such as diet and meditation. Perhaps new and gentler stratagems will be developed to assist in healing.

New research on diet, vitamins and the endocrine (hormone) system should increase our knowledge about androgenetic hair loss. However, as it is arguable whether this is a disease or a common and normal stage of maturity, there are likely to be complications arising from using drugs or genetic engineering to interfere with a natural process. Maturity can't be cured!

The development I hold out most hope for is one which would make the greatest improvement for all who suffer from hair loss. It costs nothing, requires no treatment and has no side effects. It is the development of tolerance and acceptance of all of us as the unique and interesting people we are - regardless of our appearance or how much hair we have.

BUT I DON'T LOOK LIKE ME!

Hair loss can shoot you into intimate relationships with complete strangers, just when you'd rather hide. Alopecians and their hair technologists can have a honeymoon of a time, with sensitive professionals providing sympathy and support, as well as a new image that leads to a new lease of life. Or it can be a marriage made in hell, featuring frustration, tears and debt. Here are a few points to consider in the search for a good wig and assistance to match.

You may...

- be in a state of shock or fear, having come straight from a traumatic diagnosis.

- be in the depression, denial or anger stages of grief, and therefore emotionally volatile.

- be under psychological pressure from family, school, or work.

- resent having to do this at all.

All these make the quest for the right hair replacement fraught, compared with most other tasks in life. In addition, expectations may be unrealistic. A wig will not make you look just like the old you: it is a substitute. You will have to pay for quality, if that is what you want. Hair technologists are not doctors or therapists, but business people. And you are unlikely to find the best prosthesis for you right at the start.

Tips that alopecians have found useful:

- Take a friend along for support and for a second opinion.

- Research prices beforehand to minimize shock. The more labour-intensive a prosthesis is, the more it will cost.
- Check there is a private room for fitting if you would rather not be public.
- Ask how long the wig is likely to last and how much time and money are required for upkeep.
- If you are buying an expensive custom-made 'system', get the terms (cost etc.) in writing.

Talk to the professional about your lifestyle and personality; the more information they have, the better the chance of matching your needs. If you want to be told the truth rather than be reassured or flattered, say so - and be prepared to accept it.

A cancer agency, medical specialist or support group may recommend a particularly good/cheap/sympathetic hair designer. But if you are unhappy about the goods or the service, look for alternatives. It's worth it.

Chapter 3

DOCTORS' DILEMMA

"The evaluation of a patient with alopecia must be thorough and must include obtaining a careful history and performing a good physical examination and appropriate laboratory studies. A careful review of the duration and location of the hair problem, major life changes, physical development and drug intake is indicated."

Maria K. Hordinsky, M.D. (*Dermatological Clinics*, 1987)

Hair loss is traumatic enough without the frustration of finding that the professionals you turn to for help don't live up to your expectations. This chapter looks at the reasons for 'medic headaches,' and how to improve the situation.

Dr. Hordinsky's advice is not always followed. My experience was that doctors were less thorough, and this is not uncommon. In some cases doctors fail to make a correct diagnosis, or fail to refer, and their patients discover the existence of dermatologists only through other alopecia sufferers.

Illness usually involves physical pain or discomfort. Most forms of alopecia are considered physical diseases because physical abnormalities can be observed under the microscope, and the condition sometimes responds to chemical treatment - yet the suffering is emotional, not physical. There is a deep split in orthodox health care between medicine - for diseases of the body - and psychotherapy - for diseases of the mind. So those who go to their doctor suffering from hair loss are often treated as though they have a minor ailment, but the *emotional* distress suffered is a major, often unacknowledged problem. There are, however, family doctors and specialists who recognize the need for adjustment through some form of psychological help such as counselling or self-help groups.

"In many patients [with androgenetic alopecia] the problem posed is essentially psychological and this aspect may be so predominant as to cause psychiatric disease."

Dr. R. Dawber (*Dermatologica* journal, 1987)

Dawber, co-author of *Diseases of the Scalp*, suggests that dermatologists should always refer those with alopecia for psychological assessment, because by the time they visit the specialist, patients are already anxious and may have serious problems about how they perceive their body image.

Not enough is yet understood about alopecia or cancer to allow doctors to fill their expected role of reassurance and guaranteed cure. Conventional medicine has focused on bodily processes disconnected from mental and emotional factors, which cannot be assessed by technology and the microscope. The emphasis is changing slowly in favour of prevention rather than waiting until treatment is needed, and away from reliance on drugs above all else, whether in the form of pills, lotions, creams or injections. While drugs are life-savers in such diseases as malaria, typhoid or pneumonia, the patient's responsibility for healthy lifestyle choices has often been overlooked in favour of the quick fix. Medicine is becoming big business: some drug and medical equipment companies are huge multinationals. Obviously drugs that treat rather than cure generate steady, dependable profits.

How Conventional Medicine Divorced Mind from Body

Medicine in Europe and the Arab world developed piece-meal, from herbalism, rough surgery, and religious or magical elements (spells, rituals, incantations, etc.). Healers looked at various aspects of the sick person when working out a treatment or cure. Everyday care such as colds, fevers, rheumatism, childbirth, and infant health was the domain of family members, usually women, while shamans, priests or priestesses, with their spiritual powers, looked after more life-threatening or unusual illnesses.

The earliest complete medical text was the Ebers papyrus from Egypt, written around 1600 BC but collating centuries of knowledge. It shows that the Egyptian doctor-priest listened to patients, questioned them, examined their bodies, diagnosed the problem and treated them with various compounds and regimens, diet and incantation. But as religions and societies became increasingly hierarchical, written medical knowledge and its practitioners came to be valued more highly than women healers and folk medicine.

Each culture developed its own specialization. The Hebrew (Old) Testament details rules for food handling and personal hygiene as part of the religion, and forbids the use of 'magic' in healthcare. Greek curiosity resulted in observation, speculation and deduction of principles. The Romans contributed mass preventive public health care; throughout their empire they ensured clean water supplies, built sewers, baths and hospitals. But medicine was still considered part of religion or philosophy, as was everything that we today call science.

While modern science focuses its microscope on disease (or neurosis in the mental health field), the ancient world defined health as complete equilibrium of every aspect of the person, including what we would call the mental, emotional

45

and spiritual. Personality type, diet and treatment by prayers, music or penance (where illness was thought to result from moral failings) were as important as medication.

This view of health lasted for around 2000 years, until the end of the Middle Ages, although observation and writing about disease continued. The Christian and Islamic worlds followed Jewish tradition in replacing magic with prayers. Every illness had its Christian patron saint; the fact there are patron saints of barbers but not of the bald suggests hair loss was not considered worthy of a saint's attention. (Barbers originally doubled as surgeons.)

The Divided World

Western culture has always divided the world into pairs, or opposites. It started with the Bible, with the ultimate pair of **good** vs **evil**, and **body** vs **soul**. Even now, there is a tendency to think in terms of **black** or **white**, **male** or **female**, **true** or **false**. This dualism isn't always useful, or even correct - is night really the opposite of day, or just the absence of light? Where does twilight fit in?

Not all cultures think in dualist terms - the Chinese believe that every pair contains a little of its opposite. Each male, for example, embodies female and vice versa, as represented by the Yin and Yang symbol. Their medical tradition reflects this by treating the whole person, without splitting mind and body. Current psychotherapy is often concerned with trying to integrate the parts of an individual that our culture has separated, thus acknowledging the male and female, the child and the adult, the wild and the tame, etc.

Yin Yang

Like China, the Indian subcontinent had a sophisticated civilization long before the west, and it too does not separate mind and body. Its medical tradition has always been holistic, involving diet, yoga, and meditation as well as remedies. African and First Nations (Native American) cultures are similarly all-embracing.

Up until the 16th century the Christian split between body and soul influenced medicine, yet matter was regarded as infused with the spirit of God rather than inanimate. Medicine was part of religion. The cause of some mental and physical illnesses were thought to be sinful acts, or possession by the devil. There was no such thing as 'pure' medical treatment.

In the 17th century, the split became more pronounced, with the birth of modern scientific method and rationalism. Northern Europeans began to rebel against the 'magical' elements of Catholicism, placing great significance on the material world - what they could see. The new scientific method was based on what could be seen - and preferably measured. Yet while eyes can see physical action such as blood flowing, emotions, thoughts and dreams are invisible. Non-physical symptoms, pain and other feelings are subjective and unprovable. Some scientists believed they weren't as real as the physical, visible body.

Ancient knowledge of herbs and intangible healing techniques were labelled old-fashioned, unscientific, even harmful. Competition and hostility arose between the two medical approaches that had been such useful partners. Folk medicine practitioners were individuals, often women with no formal education, while male doctors organized themselves into professional associations like the medieval guilds and guarded their specialization jealously. The witch hunts that raged through Europe, and later North America, from the 12th to the 18th centuries were aimed at such women and made it dangerous to practice folk medicine.

Descartes completed the split when he claimed in the 17th century that mind and body were two completely separate entities, a notion that still colours thinking today. Medical researchers approached the body as if it were a complicated machine. However, there is a 'ghost' permeating the machine - the mind/spirit - and very little is understood yet about how the whole person works, ghost and machine together.

During the last three centuries great steps were made in understanding and treating the mechanics of disease: bacterial scourges such as tuberculosis, smallpox and leprosy all but disappeared from much of the globe. The Industrial Revolution suggested the model of body as factory, whose processes could be analyzed and repaired for greater efficiency. This detached our bodies from our manager 'selves.'

> ### Hall of Fame
>
> HUMPHREY BOGART, film star, developed alopecia areata just before the filming of *The Treasure of the Sierra Madre*, according to Lauren Bacall's autobiography, *Lauren Bacall by Myself*

Mental and emotional factors didn't fit into an industrial model. The emphasis changed from maintaining health through diet and lifestyle (preventive medicine), to curing illness (crisis management). One unfortunate reason for this is that treating illnesses with expensive drugs and technology is more profitable than prevention.

Discoveries in quantum physics and psychoneuroimmunology are paving the way to change. Scientists no longer declare, "This is how the world is," but concede, "Given our limited knowledge, this is our best explanation to date of how things work."

Norman Cousins (in *Head First*) and other medical researchers are documenting the 'biology of hope,' or the astonishing effect positive emotions have on health. A good doctor-patient relationship helps enormously. My hope is that modern medicine will find it in its heart to become less 'clinical' and take more account of a patient's psychological state.

THE DOCTOR/PATIENT RELATIONSHIP

Problems arise if patients shy away from accepting responsibility for their own health maintenance, instead expecting doctors to act as magicians. Keeping fit, managing stress, getting enough sleep and a healthy diet are literally vital and vitalizing. Those who don't keep themselves informed, or who are not realistic in their expectations of health professionals, can let themselves in for needless frustration, anger or disillusionment.

Rehearsing a visit to a specialist with a friend or taking a friend along for support can improve communication. A useful guide is *Teamwork: The Cancer Patients' Guide to Talking with your Doctor*. Whether you are seeing a GP for a first diagnosis or a dermatologist or oncologist to discuss treatment options, the following factors in the doctor/patient relationship may come into play. If you find your doctor's attitude particularly unhelpful, it is time to search for one with whom you feel more comfortable.

Overwork

Doctors work long hours, under pressure, with enormous responsibility. Overloaded schedules make doctors rushed, and consequently less attentive. They may be too busy and preoccupied to think of all the possible causes of a complaint, and fail to explain all the options for treatment and possible side effects.

What you can do

Make a longer or double appointment with your doctor or specialist. Be prepared - use the quote at the beginning of this chapter and the tips at the end as a checklist. Write down your questions, and the doctor's answers. Be patient, patient! but be firm - it's *your* health and you deserve to get the care you need, whether it's time, attention, or clear, even repeated, explanations.

Lack Of Knowledge

Family doctors may know little about hair loss: they cannot keep up with developments in every field of illness. Major changes in understanding and treatment of hair loss have happened only recently, so were not part of most physicians' original training.

The concept of doctor as expert or father-figure and patient as ignorant or child-like is changing, but paternalistic attitudes survive here and there. Doctors need to instil confidence in their patients; some worry about admitting that they can't recognize or treat an ailment in case the patient loses faith in their professionalism.

Patients' expectations can add to the problem if doctors who admit they don't know it all are seen as third-rate. Doctors are human, too, and a few may conceal their ignorance because of previous difficult experiences with patients. Whether they admit to areas of uncertainty or not, there are doctors who react badly if you offer information or attempt to discuss your illness with them in detail.

What you can do

Take along notes, or brochures produced by support networks or specialist clinics. Ask to be referred to a specialist as soon as possible.

Doctors who get thanks rather than blame from their patients for admitting their lack of knowledge will be encour-

Vancouver General Practitioner and medical writer/ broadcaster, Dr. Art Hister, offers these tips:

- Bring along a written list of medical symptoms (and dates)
- Make your appointment at a time convenient to *you.* If you get fed up with long waits, make appointments early in the morning, before the log-jam has built up.
- If you find waiting makes you tense, take along an interesting book or magazine to occupy you
- Don't leave the doctor until you have the answers to what you want to know, for example:
    - What tests are needed and why?
    - What were the results of tests, and what does this mean?
    - How reliable are they?
    - What is the probable diagnosis and why?
    - What can I do to help my condition?
- Ask doctors to explain why they recommend certain treat- ment and what the possible side effects are.

(from *Your Better Health* magazine 3, 1990)

aged to be more open.

Being Unable to Guarantee a Cure

Doctors like to be able to help patients: it's a common reason for choosing the profession. With alopecia, however, they can't even comfort you with "You're bound to get over it," let alone offer you a sure-fire cure. When doctors cannot deliver what is expected, they may feel powerless and appear curt or even unsympathetic. They may be unsure about how to break bad news - in ancient times, such messengers were often killed.

Doctors are trained not to act on their emotions. Staying

cool is essential in coping with emergencies and rapid deci-
sion-making. Even after years of working in their field they
may not handle distress well. If they are behind schedule,
they may decide there is no time for emotional exchange, and
offer only the medical facts, the bare bones.

What you can do

Tell them you know there's no guaranteed cure before
they mention it. Your doctor can relax and communication
will be easier if you focus on what he is able to offer.

If you get upset, say so and ask for an opportunity to calm
down. Your doctor might take time to talk with you or find
someone sympathetic in the office who can spare a few minutes. Ask what is available in the way of counselling to help
you adjust.

Aarghh! Baldness!

It be wonderful if doctors were perfect medical robots,
able to respond in a kindly yet objective way to every patient.
But they can feel discomfort about baldness just like anyone
else. It's accepted that some doctors treat female patients differently from males; attitudes can affect how they treat alopecia patients too.
Medics disturbed at
the sight of a woman
who has lost some or
all of her hair may
hurry through the
appointment or be
unable to look at her
directly. They may be
very insistent that a
wig be worn, what-
ever the patient's
inclination. One

dermatologist actually refused to see patients unless they concealed their baldness.

What you can do

Assert you right to be treated professionally. After all, hair loss is just a medical problem, not a contagious mutant life form.

The Meaning of Hair, Part 2

Hippocrates, the bald 'Father of Medicine,' claimed that bald meant sexy. He believed the heat of too much 'lustful essence' caused it to rise to the scalp where it damaged the follicles.

Hair's sexual and animal associations led Buddhist monks and Christian priests and nuns to shave their heads; to show they renounced the world of the flesh in favour of the spiritual. In ancient Rome the Bald Goddess, Venus Calva, had two temples. From 1092 on, the Roman Catholic church waged war against wigs, long hair and even uncovered hair. Necessity created the unisex medieval fashion for shaving much of the head and facial hair, including eyebrows. Short hair was more convenient and healthy, and didn't show under the elaborate headdresses and hats.

Wigs were first worn in ancient Egypt, where everyone from Pharaoh to slave shaved their heads. In 1st century Rome, however, wigs were so bad that some people preferred to cover their hair loss with paint. In England, Queen Elizabeth I set the fashion for wigs. In France, King Henry III popularized wigs at his court after he lost all his hair through using unsafe dyes. Wigs became more and more outrageous until in the 18th century the biggest were hardly portable.

When the meaning of hair has to do with status and fashion, styles change rapidly. Very short hair no longer implies submission of the individual to the discipline of the group, as in the military. The association with punishment that stemmed from 'shearing' prisoners, adulteresses and Nazi collaborators has faded since punks and feminists cropped their hair willingly. Baldness is now a trend and individualism is tolerated.

Chapter 4

USING YOUR MIND

"The body often gets the message before the brain... No symptom is purely physical or purely psychological."
Christiane Northrup, MD, Fellow of the American
College of Obstetricians and Gynaecologists
(*Woman of Power* magazine 18)

The fact that we have names for different aspects of ourselves gives the mistaken impression that our bodies are somehow separate from our 'selves.' To unseparate, or complete the picture of hair loss, this chapter reviews treatments that influence the invisible elements of emotion, mind and spirit - psychotherapy and natural therapies.

Psychotherapy is a general term used for treatment given by somebody trained in the mental health field. The professional may be:

- a psychiatrist (a physician with mental health training who specializes in mental/emotional illness)

- a psychologist (someone with a degree in mental health or counselling)

- a trained counsellor (who may also be a trained physician, social worker, etc)

Holistic approaches are those which deal with the whole person, body, mind and emotions - for example acupuncture or homeopathy. This is called *fringe* or *alternative* medicine by some, because it is seen as an alternative to going to a physician. More recently, such treatment is often called *natural,* because it doesn't use manufactured drugs, or *complementary,* because it complements (adds to) your physician's care.

The Model of Health

Conventional and complementary medicine share the same basic model of health, that a person is a complex organism whose natural state is healthy. Illness occurs when the balance of health is upset for some reason, although illness, aging and death are also, as far as we know, a natural part of life. Both approaches aim to restore balance (homeostasis); the difference is in the means chosen. In practice, conventional medical treatment (apart from preventive medicine) has focused on alleviating physical conditions with drugs or with radical, pervasive treatment such as surgery, radiation or chemotherapy. Treatment tends to be standardized for everyone, whereas complementary medicine considers mind and emotions relevant, and adapts treatment to each individual, often attempting to strengthen the whole system. The ideas behind holistic medicine are becoming more popular as Western thought becomes receptive to views which are the norm in much of the rest of the world. More physicians are questioning the effects of purely drug-oriented medicine. They are accepting that disease is a function of our emotions, mental state, nutrition, personality and environment, as well as our bodies. It seems incredible today that it used to be thought that what we eat, what we feel, and what we think *don't* affect our bodies. This fundamental change of perception is still filtering through into mainstream thought.

The Holistic Approach

Holistic healers build up a picture of health using physical symptoms like pieces of the jigsaw, together with how the patient is feeling, and how their work, their family, their life is affecting them. Natural therapists usually talk with clients at length about lifestyle, diet, stress, exercise, sleep: factors the client can modify to improve their own standard of health. The well-rested, properly-fed and exercised person heightens their resistance to disease.

In the holistic perspective, you, your medical doctor and your natural therapist are partners in your health. You are the manager, the therapist is the maintenance mechanic, while the physician is the specialist technician you consult occasionally. The major responsibility is yours, because only you can feed, exercise or de-stress yourself.

Illness or pain can be seen not simply as a frightening or inconvenient situation, to erase as soon as possible with a quick fix such as an aspirin, but as a message to the body that something needs attention. In today's busy world it's easy to overlook fatigue or hunger, or to quiet these needs with a pick-up such as alcohol, coffee or junk food. Listening to your body allows you to interpret its sensations. You become aware of when things are going well and when they aren't, and by heeding warnings you can avert the worst. Smart motorists notice suspicious noises in their cars and pull over to investigate *before* the wheel falls off.

We are adaptive, self-regulating creatures - how else could our species have flourished for so long? - and need to remember the body's own healing potential, its natural inclination to health. The mind is a great ally, yet we seldom use it to its full ability in our push for better health.

The Power of the Mind

The fast-paced world of global travel, mass media and high-tech medicine as often as not ignores our immense mental powers. Technology changes so fast, and is so newsworthy, that we forget, or never discover, the real capabilities of the mind. Some physicians have started to help their patients tap into those powers, knowing that emotional and mental well-being can improve physical health. Typically they recommend stress management through counselling, relaxation, yoga, exercise, meditation, or simply getting more sleep.

Dr. Herbert Benson of Harvard Medical School is a pioneer in this field. His classic book *The Relaxation Response* details how practising deep relaxation can help the autonomic nervous system combat pain, and relieve problems such as high blood pressure. His research shows this technique can decrease tension, hopelessness and depression, and mitigate some physical effects of chemotherapy. The body has two nervous systems. One is *voluntary*, which means we can *make* our hands move, etc. The other is the *autonomic* system, which automatically runs functions such as body temperature and heartbeat. We don't control this system but imaging or meditation can influence it.

There are physicians who recommend meditation for cancer patients. Patients are taught to visualize the cancer receding or being vanquished by the body's resources. Others suggest the placebo effect is operating here. *Placebo* refers to a type of cure physicians and researchers can't explain scientifically but which has been known for centuries. Trials for new treatments often display this phenomenon. The first group of 'guinea pigs' is given the drug, e.g. a scalp lotion; the second is given the placebo - something that looks like the drug but has no medical properties; and the final group is given nothing at all. Trial after trial, some of the placebo group mysteriously get better. Since no chemical is at work, researchers explain it as the person's own expectations, hope, or faith curing their bodily illness. Some suggest the placebo effect explains how people can feel better, or even experience a cure, when they see natural therapists, take food supplements or receive spiritual or faith healing.

If your hair regrows after unorthodox treatment, you probably couldn't care less whether your dermatologist labels it placebo or not. And if the human mind is this powerful, some credit for the effectiveness of medical treatment could be assigned to the placebo effect.

PNI

The most recent development in mind-body research is the infant science of psychoneuroimmunology, or PNI, for short. Scientists are researching the links between the mind (psycho-), the nervous system (neuro-) and the immune system. The endocrine system, which produces hormones, interacts with the nervous system and the immune system. The best-known PNI researcher was Norman Cousins, whose interest in this field led him to abandon his publishing career to join the Medical School at the University of California at Los Angeles. His books present research on the healing effect of positive attitudes, including laughter. In his latest, *Head First*, he records how a six-month experiment in using imaging and other re-education methods to reduce depression in can-

> ## Hall of Fame
>
> RICK SMITH, ex-presenter of *PM Magazine*, removed his hairpiece on TV after developing alopecia areata. An ex-lawyer, Smith is now Executive Director of the Rhode Island Film Commission

cer patients led to an increase in beneficial immune cells ('killer-T'), while the control group experienced an increase in depression over the same period.

Until the late 1970s the medical establishment believed that the brain processed sensations and thoughts, and controlled body movement - but couldn't directly affect other parts of the body, such as the endocrine, immune and autonomic nervous systems. There was no scientific explanation for the bodily changes reported by people who practised meditation or yoga, or who were given hypnotherapy (or autosuggestion - using suggestion when the patient is deeply re-laxed). Now PNI is providing a scientifically acceptable ex-ploration of what holistic therapies have known and used for centuries. The 'holists' know the answer to the sum but can't explain it; the PNIers are doing the line-by-line arithmetic that explain *why* the answer is right.

The western world's historical and cultural split between body and mind is starting to heal. It is reasonable to assume the mind can help orthodox medical treatment, but is un-likely to cure illnesses such as arthritis or cancer on its own. How far the mind can affect hair growth is still hotly debated by sufferers.

Using the mind to influence emotions and the immune system is part of behavioural medicine, because it involves learning and practising new behaviours such as visualization, thus taking some control and responsibility for maintaining health. We have little control in many areas of our lives - the economy, laws, political decisions, urban development, the environment. However, research shows that the more in con-trol of their lives people feel, the healthier they are likely to be, gaining in confidence and reducing anxiety. This can have a domino effect on other areas of life.

Stress

Stress has been blamed for everything in the past decade, from headaches to alopecia to cancer.

Hair loss *always* causes stress because it is a major disrup-tion in identity. Those who think stress implies 'self-induced' need some education, and blaming a sick person for being ill only places an extra burden on the immune system. If stress were the sole cause of hair loss then the world would be full of silkheads.

When my hair first fell I thought if I removed stress from my life my hair would return. But stress is like a rock on the tracks: once it derails the train, removing the rock doesn't do the trick. Getting the train back onto the rails is a long, complex process. Working on stress seems to be a preventive rather than curative measure. It may put you on firm foundations once more, so that treatment works better, or hair that regrows has a better chance of staying. Or it may strengthen your immune system to withstand other health problems in the future.

Stress may be a contributing factor in some instances of illness, including telogen effluvium and cancer. Many alopecia areata sufferers are sure that stress was a major trigger for them, while others have no recollection of any. A university researcher who developed alopecia areata some time *after* a very stressful time in her life put forward the interesting theory that her body delayed developing the disease until it was better able to cope with it.

While managing stress cannot be depended on to cure an illness such as cancer or alopecia, it may prevent illness. Another plus is that it allows you to cope better with life in general. It can reduce the psychological trauma of alopecia.

Blame and Responsibility

In the fitness-obsessed 1980s, we were pressured into believing that everyone *ought* to be fit and healthy. Health became the new religion and those who testified that their lives have been transformed through grapefruit diets, instant enlightenment workshops or extremely expensive exercise systems claimed that if you didn't follow their exact lifestyle then you deserved every illness going.

I confess I am annoyed by those who imply that *I* caused my hair to fall out. I'm impatient with lectures from those who have no idea of what I've gone through - the pain, the horror of feeling a freak, the despair over my appearance, the frustration of trying treatment after treatment without success, the complete change my life has taken... and now the blame of the self-righteous.

"You must *want* to be bald on a subconscious level," they insist. "Haven't you tried macrobiotics/channelling/cross-training yet?"

Some people go too far. They really believe that each person is responsible for *everything* that happens to them: illness, poverty, incest, whatever. If the misguided criticize you for

External Factors Involved in Illness

- the state of the economy (boom or recession)
- technologies and their side effects
- environmental damage and pollution
- work damaging to health (computer-related complaints, irritants or poisons such as solvents or rubber)
- the stress of living in crowded, polluted, violent cities
- iatrogenic illnesses ie. those produced purely by medical treatment (eg. thrombosis from the contraceptive pill, or weakening of the body's immune system through overuse of steroids)
- heredity and genetics

your hair loss, tell them about all the good things they should be praising you for. Scapegoating - blaming the innocent for aspects of life one doesn't want to acknowledge - does not fit with aspirations towards equality and freedom. Someone who blames you for your hair loss says more about their dissatisfaction with their own life than anything about your condition.

We do have some power over our health and how we cope with stress, but blaming is not only unjust, it can negate the value of all approaches to healing. Besides, research shows that environmental factors are at the root of many incidences of cancer and other types of illness. The poorer people are, the worse their health is likely to be - regardless of region, occupation, sex or ethnic origin.

Will the holistic approach bring your hair back? Although unlikely, it is conceivable that where the follicles survive, they could be 'reactivated.' Some cancer patients claim they have visualized themselves into recoveries beyond all expectations. I have also met a couple of people with alopecia areata who say they have regrown their hair through visualization or other unconventional means. But can anyone identify with certainty what caused their hair to return?

Seeing a Psychotherapist

Woody Allen is the prototype of the neurotic New Yorker going to a 'shrink' for fifteen years to lie on couches and recount their dreams, with little to show but a big hole in their bank account...

But this stereotype is about psycho*analysis*, the ongoing analysis of mind and personality. Psycho*therapy* is a 'talking

"HARE SOUP, SIR?"

cure' to help people function better than they could before. It can take as little as a handful of visits.

There are people for whom hair loss suddenly seems bearable when psychotherapy is mentioned, because it is confused with psychiatry, and the realm of mental illness still holds an age-old stigma. In the last few decades all sorts of people have used psychotherapy to assist them in coping with all sorts of difficulties, from anxiety to sexual dysfunction. Emotional or psychological problems are no less real or valid than physical ones. As NAAF's Mental Health Handbook documents, hair loss is upsetting and seeing a psychotherapist is a legitimate way of dealing with it. If family or friends have difficulty with this, do what is best for you. When I went to see psychotherapists I explained to family and some friends what I was doing and why, but I never mentioned it at university or at work. Medical records are confidential so no one but you and your doctor need ever know.

If you require a doctor's referral, the trauma of hair loss and loss of self-esteem are ample grounds. You are likely to be seen sooner if you can afford a private therapist; a good way to find one is to ask around for recommendations, and ensure she or he is qualified.

The psychotherapist's or counsellor's role is not to solve the client's problems or tell them what to do, but to listen and help them to explore the issues and ways of functioning better.

Psychotherapists use a variety of approaches: some are non-directive - they listen and offer little feedback. Like a mental mirror, they reflect back the client's situation so it can be seen more clearly. Others take a more active part, summarizing or restating what the client tells them, so the issues and emotions appear in a new perspective. They may ask illuminating questions. They may also suggest homework such as keeping a journal, reading certain books, joining a support group or getting assertiveness training. And they may take you through the grieving process for your hair.

I have had a lot of psychotherapy and counselling over the years, and some approaches worked better for me than others. How comfortable and trusting you feel with a therapist is significant; there is no need to stay with someone who doesn't suit you.

I saw a professor of psychology who helped me realize that certain experiences - unfinished business - still cast a long shadow and that I needed to let go of guilt and be kinder to myself. He gave me biofeedback to teach me to relax, but it only made me more tense. Later I saw a psychotherapist who spent less time listening to how I felt, but succeeded in teaching me deep relaxation. She led me through a healing, calming, happy visualization and repeated this every session. She also referred me for art therapy, to help explore any unconscious factors which may have related to my alopecia.

My hair didn't grow back but I'm much less at the mercy of problems now, much less stressed and able to deal with the blues.

Choosing to see a psychotherapist or counsellor can help you get it off your chest, and do some grieving for your hair loss. It is essential not to discount the value of going through this process. In addition, you are likely to increase your self-knowledge, your confidence, and feel better about your hair loss.

Seeing a Natural Therapist

The most popular complementary therapies have been in use for a long time: acupuncture for thousands of years, homeopathy for over a century. Naturopaths use the age-old tradition of herbalism and a dietary approach. Some medical doctors also practise acupuncture or homeopathy. (The British royal family uses homeopathy.) But because there is no standard professional training in North America, it is best to seek recommendations from others. A professional body such as an association of homeopaths may be able to suggest a practitioner near you.

Read about the various alternative approaches, and talk about them with others. You should tell your family doctor you are trying something new: an open-minded physician will encourage you as long as nothing harmful is involved. The more traditional doctor may mutter about cranks and wasting money. You may be labelled a 'weirdo' but it is no more weird than trying a hair-restoring lotion recommended by a hairdresser or advertisement.

This kind of help is seldom covered by a health insurance plan. It may be out of the reach of those with low incomes, but some therapists offer a sliding fee scale, based on your financial situation.

There is no guarantee any of these methods can restore your hair, and any good therapist will tell you so. Treatment may take a few visits, or many; you decide when you want to stop. Most of these therapies are gentle and cause no side effects, unlike conventional drugs. One exception is homeopathy. The theory behind it is similar to vaccination - the homeopath gives you an extract that produces a symptom similar to one you have, hoping this will stimulate your body's defences or functions into healing. So you may experience a mild symptom: for example, when I took sulphur as a remedy for eczema, it caused an itchy rash.

Acupuncture is an ancient Chinese practice based on the view that ill-health happens when the five elements of the body (or the body's energy, *Chi*) are out of balance; inserting needles into certain points on the body opens energy channels to restore the balance. The principle of shiatsu (acupressure) is the same, but uses massage instead of nee-

ADVANTAGES	DISADVANTAGES
Medical Treatment	
• treatment is free if you have medical insurance (though drugs, lotions etc are not) • your hair is more likely to regrow than with other types of treatment • your treatment is less likely to endanger you if you get good information about side effects	• there are side effects with most treatments • hair growth is not guaranteed • you are not likely to receive much help with psychological trauma
Psychotherapy	
• should minimize or get rid of trauma • no side effects • should help with general stress; may help with other life problems • free if referred by physician (Canada, not USA)	• unlikely to restore hair by itself
Natural Therapies	
• can help deal with trauma • usually encourages you to improve general health (diet, exercise, stress) • may improve your life generally • no side effects with most approaches	• cost • no guarantee hair will regrow

SO - orthodox treatment may make you hairier but not happier; psychotherapy or alternatives, happier but not hairier!

dles. Naturopaths are licensed practitioners who advise on lifestyle and diet, and offer a variety of complementary approaches such as manipulation and Chinese medicine.

There are many psychologically-based therapies such as Gestalt, transactional analysis, psychodrama, bioenergetics, neurolinguistic programming (NLP). There are also the newer, not so well-tried *-ologies* such as iridology (diagnosis by looking at the patient's eyes). There are many other options: look through alternative healthcare guides.

If you believe faith can move mountains, spiritual (faith) healing is another possibility, whether contacting a healer from a spiritualist church or visiting a shrine such as Lourdes, France. I have heard good reports about psychodrama, a group activity where you act out roles to put you in touch with your feelings or inhibitions. One college lecturer with alopecia totalis admitted that although there was no sign of her hair returning, she had resolved a lot of past and present problems. This made the misery and anxiety of hair loss much easier for her to bear.

If you decide to try the natural medicine experience, you can expect to see a therapist for about an hour each time. You may start with one or two appointments a week, tailing off later. You'll be asked about your lifestyle, personality, past, problems, and feelings - because these elements affect your health and are used in diagnosis and treatment. They may recommend you try other types of healing, diet, meditation, etc. Because each person is different, approaches that work for some may do nothing for others, and those who share the same health problem may well be treated with very different methods or remedies.

My Experience of Natural Therapies

During the past ten years I have tried various natural therapies hoping to improve my severe eczema, asthma and hair loss. I tried three different homeopaths and some shiatsu but had no improvement in my health. Yet I have friends who have benefited enormously from these approaches, after conventional medicine had failed them.

My eczema was so bad that it made my life miserable, keeping me awake at night. My skin was always red, flaking, and gashed where I had scratched it open, often in my sleep. I had been using cortisone creams since I was a child - they no longer stopped the itching, and had damaged my skin. Doctors could offer no other solution. But after a year or so of acupuncture, the eczema gradually moved off my face and onto my back (which was hardly affected previously), then down to my feet. It then disappeared altogether, and hasn't returned. I went back for acupuncture treatments when my hair fell, but it didn't regrow. Nor did it when I visited a cranial osteopath - someone who gently massages the skull. Yet this made my asthma better than it had been for twenty years. I stopped using two types of asthma medication altogether.

Nothing made my hair return, but at least the other two health problems no longer burden my life. I improved my diet, and my immune system seems much better able to ward off the endless colds and flu I used to pick up. I felt generally supported in my quest for health.

Remember, what works for one may or may not work for another. There is no guaranteed cure for hair loss, but there is a cure for feeling bad about it. Becoming otherwise healthy, reducing stress, and expressing your emotions can make you feel much better about your lack of hair. Work on your self-esteem, and that will help you feel good about yourself and cope with other people's reactions from a position of self-acceptance.

The Meaning of Hair Part 3

When clothing is simple or non-existent, hair provides an indicator of tribe and status. Native American peoples used their complex patterns of hair and scalp decoration to distinguish each other; sometimes a particular variation was a heritage passed down through one family. African peoples exhibit many different styles; in some tribes men have the elaborate hairstyles while women shave their heads. Yet hair offends Brazilian Indians so much that they destroy it all except for protective head hair.

Whatever the attitude towards hair and the meaning assigned to it, every culture spends much free time styling, depilating, washing, treating and cutting hair. Some African tribesmen spend up to twenty hours per week attending to their hair. In many cultures, hair care and its rituals are a social event. This is a vestige of the mutual grooming typical of social animals, a bond which strengthens the group. From the earliest times when only a few people could afford sharp cutting tools, barbers have provided centres of community activity. In Elizabethan England their shops were places to hear news, make music and make merry.

When there are strict cultural interpretations of hairstyles, hair care is important. Slaves generally had to have the opposite hair and beard styles to their rulers. The Athenians looked down on the Spartans for their 'primitive' long hair. During the Civil War in England, the Roundheads saw the Cavaliers' long locks as symbolizing decadence and wealth. In the 1960s the extremes of hair on hippies and skinheads reflected the clash between their values and outlook. Perhaps losing hair is the next evolutionary step for the human race.

Chapter 5 _____

SOCIETY: WHO'S NORMAL?

"[Hair] is an odd commodity - you don't want too much
or too little and there's not too much variation on where it
could be on a man or a woman."

Dr. Vera Price, Dermatologist
(NAAF newsletter)

Only Hair?

Possessing head hair is just one cultural norm among many
to do with appearance. Men should develop hair on their
face, women shouldn't, except for eyebrows and eyelashes.
Men should have hair on their body, women shouldn't, except for the pubic region. Men should have thick eyebrows
and short eyelashes, women should have slender brows and
thick eyelashes. Having too much hair can be as much of a
problem as having too little; I discovered this through meeting British writer, Jill Miller, who was planning a book on
women who see themselves as too hairy.

Hair is the most distinctive physical characteristic of humans. Skin colour and ethnic characteristics come close, and
height, build, eye colour - but none of these is as useful as
hair. It can distinguish one person from another at a distance,
and holds more obvious individuality than skin and facial
features. In spite of wild variations in amount and location of
hair in individual men and women, hair is still classed as the
second most important sexual characteristic - i.e. the second
main way men and women differ, physically. In other words,

hair separates the men from the boys and the women from the men.

It can signal gender, adulthood, ethnic background, age, values, conformity to gender standards and subculture. Hardly 'only' a wad of mostly dead fibrous stuff! Hair both suggests your allegiances - who and what you identify with and your outlook on life - and is a means of self-expression too. Writers like Raymond Chandler use hair to convey personality; with the labels 'sultry brunette' or 'redhead' the reader gets an instant picture. It is one of the aspects of our physical appearance that is most changeable and within our control, a bridge between the self and society. No wonder we lose a lot when we lose hair.

When you start to lose your hair, you lose part of your identity. One young woman who lost most of her hair through crash dieting put it this way:

"I didn't really think I was up to much before - you know, I wasn't together, successful, full of energy - and I was always trying to diet. But when my hair started to disappear, I had to get a wig. I thought I looked like a freak, a sort of sub-human, even though I didn't let anybody see me without my wig. It was as if I'd been victimized by God, like some sort of joke."

The concept of a human being always includes hair. Only new-born babes and very old men are expected to be bald. *Woman* implies strokeable, attractive hair as part of the image, even personality. *Man* implies a certain animal virility which seems incompatible with baldness. And as soon as your hair starts to fall, everywhere you look you notice hairdressers, advertisements for hair products, manes of hair tossing all over the TV, films and magazines.

Suddenly your looks are too different for comfort; you encounter some curious reactions from strangers and from those you know. Some are uncomfortable because hair loss makes them think of chemotherapy or AIDS - illness and even death. Unintentionally and unwillingly disturbing those around you simply by your appearance can be mortifying. Explaining an obscure condition like alopecia areata is hard because it's not yet understood, or even proven to be a single disease. And ignorance about female pattern baldness can suggest the condition is "abnormal" rather than a natural feature of maturity.

When your image changes suddenly and you are still in a state of shock, it isn't easy to keep perspective. You may think

Hall of Fame

PETE GARRETT of top Australian band MIDNIGHT OIL has shaved his head for over 14 years. It's "one less thing to worry about." A qualified lawyer and one-time senatorial candidate, he is president of the Australian Conservation Foundation

you are the only weirdo in a world of normal people. But *normal* means simply standard or expected: it has nothing to do with worth. The worth of a pearl is based on its being rare, *un*usual. The world is so full of choices and information that we set up our own shorthand system. Habits and routines allow us a rest from making decisions every few minutes. The picture we build of 'normality,' or what is standard, allows us to ignore much of our perception so we only have to process what *doesn't* fit our expectations. When expectations are fulfilled, we feel secure and comfortable. It gives us a sense of control and predictability. But the more closely normal people are scrutinized, the more unusual everyone appears. In fact, a normal person - someone with no quirks or surprises - is a real abnormality. As poet Lee Maracle observes, "No one is normal, but we're all natural."

Fitting In

Why should losing an inert, physically unnecessary part of your body be traumatic? After all, people seldom get depressed about losing their appendix. The visibility of the loss and the loss of part of one's public image are part of the story.

Much has to do with *fitting in*. Humans have two conflicting urges: to fit in, and to stand out. We all want to have hair, limbs, to be within a certain height range - to be 'one of the gang' with our social circle. And we want to be seen as individuals, without losing acceptability. For example, women don't want to wear exactly the same suit, blouse and jewellery as their colleagues.

Humans are 'tribal' creatures, needing contact with our kind from birth. Very few ever choose to live completely isolated from other people, though some prefer to keep company at arm's length. (Henry Thoreau, a classic example, wrote about his nineteenth century experiment in solitary self-sufficiency in *Walden*.) Most of us need people, emotionally, socially, psychologically, physically. We gain enormous benefits from living among our own species, whether we're in a scarcely populated farming community or a hectic, crowded city. But we pay a price for company: a degree of conformity. Most societies have laws which, together with the constitution, form the framework we have to abide by if we want to live with others.

Society and culture also create pressures on us. Families, workplace, religion, groups of friends all push members to conform. Employees are expected to share certain values or attitudes, to vote like other union members, or to send their children to private schools as the other managers do. Groups of friends and other peer groups have unspoken rules about appearance or behaviour, such as what to wear and how to act at a concert, at work, to a wedding.

It takes a strong sense of self to stand out from the crowd and stand up to pressure, whether it's saying no to drugs, being a pacifist or choosing an unusual job. Those who 'stick out' often gain confidence and an inner strength, but their lives are seldom as easy as if they blend in. Wherever you turn, somebody's expecting you to be a certain kind of person, and people who lose their hair don't fit in in the way they're expected to.

Why We Want to Fit In

It's an essential part of human psychological development to want to fit in. Psychologist Abraham Maslow observed that we have a hierarchy of needs. When our needs are satisfied at one stage, we tend to move on to the next. Psychologist John Rowan clarified the last stage by quoting a friend:

> "I was fed up with playing parts in other people's movies: I wanted to start writing my own movie."
>
> *I-to-I* magazine (UK)

According to where you are in life's journey, hair loss will affect you differently. If you get your self-esteem primarily from doing what others expect of you, hair loss can hit hard. As one bank executive comments:

> "You could say I'm a normal kind of guy. I did the right things, went to school, got my training, doing well. That's the kind of life I want. I want to be comfortable, and I'm a good provider for my wife and children. I just couldn't deal with it when I got these bald patches. I'm only 31. Now I'm nervous about my prospects and I don't seem to have anyone I can talk to about this. I think I've really let my family down."

Everybody is discouraged from living a life without limits,

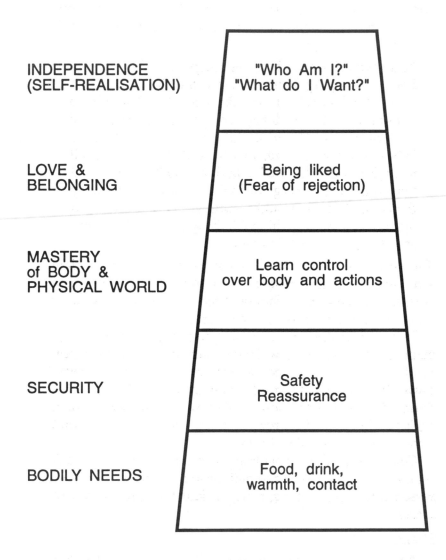

INDEPENDENCE
(SELF-REALISATION)

"Who Am I?"
"What do I Want?"

LOVE &
BELONGING

Being liked
(Fear of rejection)

MASTERY
of BODY &
PHYSICAL WORLD

Learn control
over body and actions

SECURITY

Safety
Reassurance

BODILY NEEDS

Food, drink,
warmth, contact

HIERARCHY OF NEEDS

and encouraged to get their self-esteem through pleasing others, but the expectations are highest for women, particularly in the realm of image:

> "I always did what other people expected of me, *always*. I was moving up in my career in the beauty business when I got cancer. It was the first time I started to question what I was doing with my life, and why. The change in my looks really hit me, it was frightening. When my hair fell out, that was it. I wanted to kill myself. But then I started to find out - in therapy - what was underneath my good looks. I broke up with my fiance and went through a pretty shaky period, but now I'm doing something I'd always secretly wanted - studying to be a veterinarian."

If it weren't the trauma of hair loss, some other crisis might well precipitate similar anguish, fear and self-doubt: the death of someone close, being laid off after years of loyal work, or children growing up and leaving home.

In my case, the loss of an important part of my image made me realize just how little confidence I had in myself, and how much I depended on those around me for approval. I was like a mirror that could shine only with light reflected from other people. Hair loss pushed me to cultivate my own neglected light, until it grew stronger and I realized I didn't have to depend on others to shine.

Confidence is not something we're born with - it's a skill we must practise in order to build a solid foundation for our personalities. It's not a gift but a skill that improves with practice.

Shame

Anxiety, fear, distress are expected results of any loss, but shame and humiliation occur too, stemming from our natural desire to fit in. Shame is one of those deep-seated, intense emotions that often seems illogical. Therapist and writer John Bradshaw calls it a toxic emotion because it can poison our lives and freedom. Shame is something we're taught very early, by our closest family members, and by teachers. It's not a natural instinct but an emotional state fostered by social groups to persuade us to conform.

The combination of disapproval and secrecy seems to be what produces shame. Many people can recall instances when they were punished in front of others at school when young, before they learned what was acceptable to adults. Public humiliation often deepens the shame. Hair loss revives that old fear of exposure to judgment. It recreates the anxiety that people will disapprove and stare, and suggests that secrecy means safety. Losing hair means we lose face and lose pride in our appearance and success. We have suddenly dropped way down the social heap.

Because there's nothing morally wrong about losing hair (it's not breaking the law), shame is an inappropriate response.

Fear of Rejection

Shame and fear of rejection are linked: if we don't fit in we fear being ostracized from the group. This primitive fear is mirrored in the animal world: an albino crow is harassed by its own group, perhaps in part because its conspicuous contrast might endanger the group's safety. Such fear is well-founded with hair loss, because rejections can and do occur. But however troubling curiosity and embarrassment are, they should not be confused with rejection.

I feared stares, whispers, gossip, verbal attacks. Yet most people I encounter are too busy with their own pursuits or problems to be deeply concerned at my alopecia. Unattached silkheads are afraid they will never find a partner. Married ones fear their partner cannot possibly continue to love them, and will leave them for someone who looks 'normal.' Yet as a husband in his forties said in some frustration: "I don't know why she keeps pushing me away and telling me it's impossible I can still love her. I didn't marry a hairstyle, I married a person!"

Young people at school fear insensitivity from teachers, taunts and even physical attacks from other children. Adults feel they have aged twenty years overnight.

The fear of being an outcast is socially and emotionally disabling. When my hair first fell out I stayed in the house as much as possible. Some people give up their job, others limit their social lives. Hair loss makes us shy and introverted. Many people with disabilities suffer from this too; segregation damages both those shut away and the rest of society. It gives a false picture of what is human and natural. Integration is the only practical solution for an ever more varied population.

Looking Different

Very few people ever feel completely happy about their appearance, even when they have hair. A number of people, both men and women, have wryly commented that they never appreciated their hair until it was gone.

"Before I lost my hair it used to drive me nuts. It never did what I wanted. It was wiry and hard to handle and always too dry. When I styled it, it would stay for a couple of hours - till the

---

Hall of Fame

MICHAEL JORDAN led the Chicago Bulls to their first National Basketball Championship. Possessor of an aerodynamic headshave that keeps him light on his feet, Jordan was recently voted one of *People* magazine's 10 best dressers.

79

wind blew, or humidity got too high, or it rained. I complained about it all the time. I was always trying different colours as well, because it was kind of mousy."

Some people find that losing their hair makes them appreciate their body more. Most, however, first go through a stage of extreme distress. "I never looked good before, but now I'm hideous," is a common reaction. But we're all hard on ourselves, even fashion models. I had to laugh when I read that Marie Helvin, top model of the 70s and 80s, complained that her legs are too long.

Our feelings and judgements about our appearance are *relative*. If losing hair makes you more appreciative of the rest of your body, in time you will become used to your head.

And if beauty is in the eye of the beholder, so is ugliness. As Morris Rosenberg observes,

"If we say someone is 'ugly,' we are providing a much better description of *our* feelings than of his appearance."

Conceiving the Self

People without hair look different and unusual, but different doesn't mean ugly. First and foremost we have to deal with our *own* critical inner voices. Gill Ridington in a paper for the Disabled Women's Network of Canada comments,

"If we can learn to feel good about ourselves, everything else will fall into place."

Self-Image and Women with Disabilities

The Inner Critic

When somebody suffers prejudice or discrimination simply because of how they look, they can 'internalize' this rejection, becoming convinced they are worth less. Self-esteem drops. Even if those around us are towers of strength after we lose hair, we can still feel inadequate. The story of Cyrano de Bergerac is the perfect example of how somebody who looks different assumes he is, therefore, inferior. The story was modernized in the film *Roxanne*, with Steve Martin as the fireman C.D. Bales. It tells how a wonderful man cannot believe any woman could ever love him, because his nose is so big.

We've all internalized numerous 'put-down' messages about ourselves, messages that come from the majority culture's values and prejudices. What these messages are vary according to gender, age, ethnic background and the groups we are part of. These change with time and do not reflect the *truth* about us.

We know attitudes and criteria do change, and as they do, the inner criticisms diminish or disappear. Forty years ago a divorce was rare and disgraceful. Today, with one in three marriages breaking up, divorce is a generally accepted part of life and divorced people are seldom pressured into believing they are worthless.

Much of what's normal today won't be in twenty years time. Walking around openly bald would have been impossible for most people in the long-haired sixties and seventies. As with other social changes, those who defy the social pressures to look 'nice' and expect to be accepted as they are, without pretence, are starting to change cultural attitudes. With increasing numbers of people undergoing chemotherapy, and the trend towards shaved heads started by the punk movement, a bald head isn't the complete shock it once was.

We all fall into one minority or another, but some minorities are tolerated better than others. There is no longer much prejudice against people who wear glasses, but hair is another story. Although you can hide your baldness with a wig, you still have to live with the possibility of your cover being blown, sometimes literally. You can't always choose to 'come out' when you judge it's safe. Even if those around you are supportive, advertising, social traditions and fashion trends

Men's headwear
of the Italian
Renaissance

GIOTTO.

MICHAEL ANGELO.

DANTE.

82

create standards and pressures that can make you feel inferior to *anyone* with hair, no matter how gifted or lovely you are.

Covering - Protection or Hiding?

Shame and fear motivate us to cover our difference, even though it is no more logical to feel ashamed of alopecia than of hay fever. But there are other reasons to cover up and great debates rage over the issue. We all have different lives with different constraints, values and people to fit in with. Each of us has to look at our reasons for our choices, and find the way that feels comfortable and 'us.' Are we making our decision based on our needs, or to please others or because we think we *ought*?

One television star spoke to me only on condition he remain anonymous. A few months after alopecia areata struck he decided he would like to go public to raise awareness about the condition. But his agent told him it would be career suicide. In order to continue in the career he loves and provide for his family, he has to live with what he described as discomfort, anxiety about being found out, and a feeling of being a fraud - not being true to himself.

Once we find a certain way to cope with hair loss, it can stop us from exploring other options. The most rewarding approach is to go for choice rather than rule. Some decide that certain situations demand certain images. Many people who wear a wig to work or when out with friends, wear a baseball cap while playing sports, a cap or turban on the beach, and a scarf or nothing at home. Either way - protecting or uncovering - can, depending on personality, situation and motives, allow us to feel more in control over this thing that happened against our will, which increases our sense of power and self-esteem.

"Now I've got used to wearing a wig I've started to

have fun. I have different ones so I can change my image any time. Some people think I'm crazy but I may as well make the most of it."

Hair loss forces us to be non-conformists to some extent. It seems ironic that in the so-called "free world" so few of us feel free to be different, free to be ourselves. If we'd *chosen* to express ourselves by shaving off our hair - like Sinead O'Connor and so many others in the entertainment field - we'd be happy about our trendy image and get a kick out of other people's reactions. Above all, we would know that we could regrow it when we wanted. But because it happens against our will, we feel victimized and sometimes blame our poor defenceless, interesting heads.

The British talk show on hair loss in which I appeared included people of every possible view:

"We owe it to ourselves to look as good as we can," said one woman in a very glamorous wig. "It means we can lead a normal life and carry on working. Heavens, with the wigs available today we can look *better* than we ever did before all this happened!"

"Well wearing a wig made me feel I had something to hide," countered a young woman who was shortly to get married - wearing a scarf. "I don't think alopecia is anything to be ashamed of. I never felt comfortable. Now I've thrown my wig away I'm sort of - more *me*. It makes me feel freer."

"So why are you wearing a scarf?" asked a smartly-dressed woman in a wig. "You're hiding just as much as anyone with a wig."

"No, it's different," interrupted another scarf wearer. "If you wear a wig, you're pretending that you still have hair. But if you wear a scarf, it's obvious you don't."

"I don't know why you all think you have to wear something on your head," said a striking-looking model. "People look really good without hair. I've shaved all mine off and I

Covering vs Uncovering

Covering:

- allows us to fit in
- helps us adjust if hair loss is sudden
- may be essential for work & some social activities
- protects from sun
- keeps head warm
- protects from unwanted stares and comments

Uncovering:

- allows us to adapt to how we actually look now
- allows us to feel accepted for ourselves/just as we are
- can be liberating after wearing a wig/hat
- encourages others to communicate with us
- gives opportunity to educate others about alopecia
- looks striking, brings compliments
- no limits on activities, sporting and otherwise

enjoy it. I walk down the street and people look at me, they tell me how good I look. Why not enjoy it?"

Indignation erupted from all corners of the audience - "You've chosen to do it!" "You can't know what it's like for us - your hair can grow back any time you want to let it."

The show's presenter - who had suffered the odd bald patch herself a few years before - turned to me, the only openly bald woman there. "Isn't there too much fuss about wigs?" she asked. "Don't you think that people who wear wigs are silly?"

"No, I don't think they're silly," I replied. "I think everyone should have the choice whether to wear a wig or a scarf, or not. But the problem is, the way things are at present, most of us aren't really free to choose."

Degrees of Openness

Feeling powerless to talk about something - to 'name' a deep change that has happened to you - can also keep shame in place. And shame is intimately involved in low self-esteem. So whether you uncover or not, it is most important to open up and "confess" the terrible sin of hair loss. This involves risk and vulnerability, for you and the others in your life. It can upset ingrained habits and expectations, like a homosexual 'coming out.' This is where your attitude counts, because if you do this out of acceptance mellowed with understanding of the challenge you are asking of family and friends, they are likely to help you along the way.

At first it was not easy for my family and friends to go out with me and see others staring; but just as I have become used to the looks and don't even notice them most of the time, so have my family and friends adjusted.

There is a tendency to think that others have to be protected from the naked truth. One woman who has been active in alopecia work for years still does not let her husband see her without a wig, even in bed. Another has not told her children that her 'hair' is a wig. In these situations, protecting others is often a complexity of emotions, including fear of rejection and loss of youth, or fear of being unlovable.

The whole premise of *the* expert on loss, Dr. Elisabeth Kubler-Ross, is that most people, whatever their age, can handle the truth and have the right to be given that opportunity. Protecting others from the truth implies you don't trust their ability to cope with or adapt to your loss. If you have ever been misinformed about medical matters or about the impending death of a parent, you might have felt patronized or insulted, rather than protected. Trust that others are capable of coping with real life. They deserve that dignity and respect.

Protecting others may stem from an unadmitted desire to protect ourselves from the awkwardness of having to talk about the real situation. Another motive may be to hold on to what little control we can still keep around our hair loss: control over other people's reactions.

"Only my sister knew about my hair. I couldn't tell anyone else. Then I started going steady with one special man, and didn't want my alopecia to jeopardize our relationship. After a while I wanted to tell him but couldn't, because it would look like I'd been lying to him all this time. One evening I got too carried away to be "on guard" and my wig slipped over my eyes! The funny thing was, he said he'd known about my wig for ages and was very worried because he thought I must have cancer but didn't trust him enough to tell him. He was so relieved it was just female pattern alopecia!"

Richard Sandomir, author of *The Hair-Raising Adventures of Baldman*, admits he felt "totally paranoid" about his toupee. For him, deciding to go *au naturel* allowed him a dignity he didn't find while worrying about involuntary exposure and possible ridicule. 'I look at my toupee [now unused] and say 'I've won'," he proclaimed in the BBC/Nova video *Sex Lies and Toupee Tape*.

The more the public knows about alopecia areata, the more acceptable it will become. It's a tribute to the human spirit, its courage, hope, determination and ingenuity that I have met so many strong, delightful, beautiful people who suffer from hair loss. They have open minds and hearts, they have thought deeply and learned from their experiences. Social constraints can and will continue to be fought.

Chapter 6 _____

THE MAGIC OF IMAGE

"Oppressed Hair Puts a Ceiling on the Brain"

Alice Walker

Image Mania

The word *image* comes from the Latin *imago*, which meant imitation or copy, such as a picture or statue. Nowadays its meaning has expanded to include:

- appearance
- the pictures on TV and film screens
- the impression a person makes, including appearance and behaviour
- lifestyle
- marketing profile

Image is a form of short-hand mass communication that doesn't even require awareness of the 'audience.' At times it is our main outlet for creativity and individuality, and a means of self-expression. We all make snap judgements based on appearance, often unconsciously, with hair, face and clothes being the most important aspects.

Image plays a big role in how we feel about ourselves. A classic sign of depression is when people stop caring about how they look. That's why any sudden change in image creates emotional turmoil and a period of adjustment - until we become familiar with the new self. Adapting to a new image is a process that requires courage and persistence. The more is invested in image, the harder uncontrollable change can be to handle. Oddly enough, if hair regrows the old, once-familiar look can be difficult to adjust to also.

> "I have longed for my hair to regrow for years. But now it's back, I'm not as happy as I expected. It's so short, still, and maybe I'm so used to wearing wigs now. I don't think my real hair looks as good as my wig, and I don't really want to stop wearing my wig. It's crazy."

Trying to adjust to my hairless look reminded me how strange and ugly I thought my body was when it started to change at puberty. At first I didn't want that extra hair on my body. But as time passed I became familiar with my body, then began to appreciate it and finally accept it as part of myself, rather than dissociating 'me' from 'my body'.

Hair is both part of the body and decoration: it's the one bit we can 'dress up' or down without using clothing or ornaments. Silkheads often have more flexibility about image than Before the Fall. Wearing wigs can emphasize different qualities: sophisticated, carefree, efficient or youthful. Head-scarves or turbans can look conventional, bohemian or glamorous, while caps or hats can be ordinary, elegant, sporty, or trendy. With a head that is mostly bare, not covering it expresses strong individuality - "This is me, take it or leave it"; sometimes vulnerability (like Sinead O'Connor), or toughness (like Telly Savalas' Kojak character) or an exotic appeal (Yul Brynner). For those who prefer less attention, the skills of beauty professionals, from hair technologists to make-up artists, enable alopecians to feel happier about their looks.

Yet image can become a prison. In these days of mass communication, image has become ever more crucial. The most subtle values, the unspoken pressures to conform, are so rooted in daily life that we are hardly aware of them.

North Americans are raised on a diet of television, films, magazines, advertisements, and the millions of images they present. In this age, achievement and image are life's most important goals, or so it's suggested in the mass media. Everywhere we look there are idealized images - 'imitations' - of successful, attractive people. Even with a full head of hair, you can feel as though you never quite live up to your potential. The ads suggest you're missing out. So when your hair goes, to feel insecure, afraid, even a freak is not really surprising. You are swimming against a powerful tide.

The Beauty Myth

"You owe it to yourself," is the line the advertisers use to sell products, "you *deserve* this hair gel or colorant." But if there isn't much (or any) hair to style, it can seem as though you don't deserve anything at all because you're not attractive enough. This is known as the 'beautiful equals good' myth, and it affects all of us.

Men were once immune from image pressure. Grooming - being clean and tidy - was all a straight man needed; anything more and there might be gossip about his sexual orientation. But hair transplantation is now the most common cosmetic surgery in the world (almost all clients are men) and male facial cosmetic surgery is on the rise.

The concept of beauty is one of the most changeable in the world. Any National Geographic or out-of-date fashion magazine proves the point. Beauty standards are made by people, not made in heaven; one decade's 'Face' is the next one's peculiarity.

A careful look at our era and culture can help us realize that this too is merely a temporary picture, as changeable as TV or films. Every period of history, every culture, has had its own set of priorities and values.

Beauty today has as much to do with politics and profits as with aesthetics; it's supposedly available to everyone with enough money and time. Naomi Wolf's *The Beauty Myth* (Chatto and Windus, 1990) quotes Dr. Arthur K. Balin, President of the American Aging Association:

"It would benefit physicians to look upon ugliness not as a cosmetic issue but a disease."

But as a comedian once said,

"If we all liked the same thing, everybody would be after your grand-mother."

Beauty is more than a visual quality. It includes personality, charm, grace, voice, humour, intelligence and many other indefinable qualities. Confidence, popularity, love and sexiness can be ours at any age, whatever our looks, and such qualities do not fade.

> ## Hall of Fame
>
> STEVEN JONES, hat creator for top fashion designer Katherine Hamnett, shaves his head as a fashion statement.

Image can be a fun, enjoyable means of adding to our self-esteem, or it can turn into an obsession. Wolf observes that women have moved from having the 'double shift' of house management and child-rearing plus career, to shouldering the 'third shift' - all the time, money and energy spent on keeping our bodies and image professionally fit and perfect. This is a recent trend, borne out by advertising figures. In recent, random issues of the women's magazines *Redbook* and *Cosmopolitan* I discovered that over half the ads are for cosmetic products or services, and 12 - 17 per cent of those are for hair products. Yet in the 1950s the majority of women's magazine ads were for household products, while time-consuming beauty routines were used mostly by those whose profession depended on

The Beauty Business: Annual Turnover
Diet industry: 33 billion dollars
Cosmetics industry: 20 billion dollars
Cosmetic surgery industry: 20 million dollars

their image, such as models or actors. Wolf relates:

> "A gray-haired editor for a leading women's magazine told a gray-haired writer that an article about the glories of gray hair cost her magazine the Clairol account [advertising revenue] for six months."

Perhaps this explains why alopecians are invisible in print except as 'triumphs over tragedy.' Even the models that make it into magazines are not originals. Wolf quotes Bob Ciano, ex-art director of _Life_ magazine:

> "No picture of a woman goes [photographically] unretouched."

The Eleventh Commandment

Standards of beauty existed in earlier times but they weren't promoted relentlessly. A few decades ago, social pressure focused on respectability rather than on looking young. People were ashamed, depressed or penitent about their behaviour. Now these morals have been transferred to the body: we feel bad about our flab, we are penitent about eating and depressed at our wrinkles. 'Thou shalt look good' has become the eleventh commandment, as if _looking_ good equals _being_ good. Linda Tschirhart Sanford and Mary Ellen Donovan point out:

> "200 years ago many American families did not have mirrors in their homes, and a woman might well have gone through her daily routine week after week without

inspecting her image in a looking glass."

Women and Self-Esteem

Nowadays, of course, there are mirrors in every home, every store, and every washroom, in cars, restaurants, shopping malls and offices. We can't escape seeing our image unless we head for the wilderness.

As technology pervades every sphere, being human seems almost too biological, too limiting. When health and beauty are defined as looking young, people can become obsessed with trying to make time stand still by keeping their body thin, face unwrinkled, hair anything but grey. So they march forward with their faces turned back to the past, towards the way they used to look. Refusing to face the fact that age and death are inevitable is a denial of humanity, which can result in diminished interest and hope in the future, as well as distorted values.

Those who suffer from cancer know just how taboo a subject death is, and for many decades the shame that accompanies a taboo clung to cancer. (In contrast, in Victorian times death was often seen as romantic, and was a subject of enormous interest.) Loss of hair is usually associated with the elderly, so acts as a reminder of aging and therefore death. The rise in cancer occurrence and treatments that result in hair loss has strengthened this association. The equation of health and youth with attractiveness means that if we and others associate our hair loss with illness or aging, we conclude we must be unattractive, whatever we actually look like.

One potent cultural norm is that men and women must look and behave very differently. Yet rock stars - David Bowie in his earlier years, Annie Lennox, Sinead O'Connor, Prince, bands like The Cure and Kiss - are popular with young rebels precisely because they break this rule and blur the boundaries between masculine and feminine. Although we celebrate the differences between men and women, in the global view the two sexes have far more similarities physically, mentally and emotionally, than differences.

What is the essence of being female or male, beyond the visible signs such as appearance? It can be useful to make a list of characteristics you consider male, and those you consider female. Check the people you know against the list: it's surprising how few qualities are restricted to one sex. Make a list of your good qualities, too - the ones that don't require hair. The more we work on feeling good about ourselves, the less we need constant approval from outside to give us confidence. We gain serenity, a balanced perspective and independence.

Hair Loss and Femininity

Women fear that without hair they won't look feminine; in fact, they may feel 'neutered,' barred from enjoying their femininity.

When my hair fell I was working in computers, where appearance and femininity were not so important. Although I thought I wasn't that concerned about my appearance, I suffered anguish over feeling asexual, as though it was only my hair that had made me a woman.

Far more is made of women's appearance than men's. It starts long before puberty, with girls being praised for how they look while boys are praised for their actions, boldness or brains. It's not just a woman's innate delight in colour and beauty that makes her want to decorate herself, but social expectations and the 'positive strokes' she gets from others. Some women feel forced into society's idea of what looks feminine because otherwise they get unwanted comments from those they know. Those who feel unfeminine without make-up and heels may find hair loss undermines their very sense of who they are. But if you feel like a real female only when you are pleasing an audience, you're doing yourself an injustice. Being a woman is natural and should be a joy, not an obligation.

I have adopted as new role models women who work out what kind of dress and behaviour please *themselves*, too. It's a growing trend: even television is progressing beyond the identification of female with glamour, with programs like *Golden Girls, Roseanne*, and *Babes*.

Some women spend years growing their hair. If it all falls, they have lost all that investment. If they develop small bald patches, when that hair regrows it will be the wrong length, and a work of art has to be rethought. A dancer who developed cancer found the loss of her extremely long hair the most devastating part of the illness. This determined woman coped with the disease and its treatment, but her hair was symbolic of her vocation. She has no assurance it will reach the same length again, and how many years this might take.

Luckily, losing a crowning glory allows us to see other, more subtle aspects of ourselves overlooked when we were blinded by the glitter in the mirror. Eventually I recovered my enjoyment of clothes and jewellery, and felt feminine and sexy once more, but now enriched by the personal strengths that hair loss drew out.

Many women with just partial hair loss merely rethink their hairstyle. Cut short, permed or styled with a wave to increase the appearance of fullness, hair can be attractive yet easy to look after. And although it never makes up for the real thing, make-up can cover the absence of eyebrows and lashes.

Hair Loss and Masculinity

Women who lose hair may assume it's easier for men - but that's not always so. The most reproduced picture in the world is the head of a bald man who wore a wig to face the world. It's George Washington on the US $1. Although more importance is attached to women's appearance, men still *want* to look good, both to be accepted as 'one of the boys' and to be sexually attractive. Losing hair makes some men feel less virile and young. One systems analyst in his forties comments:

> "When I started losing my hair, I wished I was a woman. Really! They can wear make-up and wigs and nobody gives them a second thought. I can't do *anything* about my eyelashes or put make-up on the half eyebrow that's gone. I just hope people don't notice, because of the glasses I wear. I'd sooner use contacts, but these seem

Washington with and without

safer. People can tell, though - sometimes I see people looking at my hairpiece. My wife thinks I'm vain to worry about it, but she doesn't understand women aren't the only ones who are sensitive."

Men just can't win. No matter how they deal with alopecia, there will be other guys making jokes about it, scoring points in the macho contest. If men allow hair to disappear without seeking treatment, people might judge them to be 'past it', in terms of energy, youth, success, and sex. If they use prostheses such as a hairpiece or 'weave', they put up with jibes about being effeminate - paying too much attention to appearance, 'like a woman'. And if they boldly shave their heads, regaining some sense of control over their appearance, they worry about being labelled skinhead or weirdo; teenagers and men of African descent are the only groups at present that seem to enjoy the stylishness of shaved heads. Yet when alopecia universalis sufferer Mark Murphy played football for the Green Bay Packers, he was often asked if he shaved his head to make him look more macho.

Because body hair appears at puberty when boys become sexually mature, hair is equated with potency. Quite illogically, loss of head hair is assumed to mean loss of virility - yet male pattern baldness occurs partly because of higher amounts of the male hormone testosterone.

Every man knows he is likely to lose hair at some point in his life, yet few are prepared for this - or for the dejection that can follow. It's male clients who generate most of the hair loss industry's profits. Richard Sandomir, in *The Incredible Adventures of Bald Man*, wryly documents the turmoil, denial, humiliation and patronizing treatment he encounters in search of treatment or a hairpiece that really fits. The impact of assuming that men's hair symbolizes virility is illustrated by the story of Samson in the Hebrew (Old) Testament. Whether Samson's strength literally lay in his hair or not, once Delilah had cut it off he *believed* he was no longer manly and strong.

Another literary reflection of the relation of hair to virility appears in Gabriel Garcia Marquez' novel *Love in the Time of Cholera* (Alfred Knopf, 1988). Florentino is a man who suffers unrequited love for one woman most of his life, even while he conducts numerous affairs with other women. Yet "his greatest battle... was against baldness. From the moment he saw the first hairs tangled in his comb, he knew that he was condemned to a hell whose torments cannot be imagined by those who do not suffer them." Marquez goes on to detail Florentino's strategies against hair loss, including trying 172 'infallible' cures. After a gibe from a drunk, Florentino finally cut off his remaining hair and "embraced with all his heart his destiny of total baldness... and attributed to it the masculine virtues that he had heard about and scorned as nothing but the fantasies of bald men."

Men have to deal with a double problem - the hair loss and the conditioning to 'tough it out.' They are expected to suffer in silence despite their feelings. Men may find it harder to go through the stages of grieving or to talk to friends about what's deeply personal. They are seldom used to seeking help of the sort available from support groups. Just as it's a huge effort for women to believe that men find them feminine and sexy even without hair, so men may have to struggle to believe women when they say they find male silkheads a 'turn on.' Yet in 1991 Dr. M. Wogalter conducted a study on appearance that reported men with little or no head hair are seen as intelligent, mature and "not unattractive," while men with beards are much less attractive (*Journal of Social Psychology*).

It takes courage to withstand pressure from peer groups about looking different. Boys and men who have created close non-macho relationships with other males, where they are accepted for who they are, have an easier time. The less attachment there is to a 'masculine' image, the more attention and energy is available for coping with hair loss. The Bald Headed Men of America's aim is to embrace their baldness with zest, transforming a loss into a feature: "No drugs, plugs or rugs."

Hair Loss and Aging

Almost everyone, male or female, gradually loses hair as they age. Whether we put it in these terms or not, "growing older is, after all, everyone's goal," states psychologist Harriet Goldhor Lerner in an article in *New Woman* magazine. She asks, "Why would we choose to perpetuate the notion that there is anything shameful or lesser in growing older?" Older people are still valued advisers in some communities ('senator' is the Latin for 'elder'), whatever the state of their hair and teeth. These days seniors are working, working out and joining the 'Grey Panthers'. People are living longer and healthier lives, and research reports that as they age, the majority becomes more content with their lives, not less. The picture of lively seniors whom I know is one I like to remember when I look in the mirror and feel fear of change, of aging.

Hair loss for men can come at a challenging time. It's often when they have the most responsibility at work and home, with children growing up and demanding more, financially and emotionally. The questions "Is this all there is? Is it downhill from now on?" can haunt them.

Female pattern baldness can strike women at a crucial time of their lives. The physical and hormonal changes of menopause, with the loss of fertility, can induce insecurity about femininity. When hair loss accompanies these major body changes, the sense of deprivation can be crushing.

"I was going through great rushes of emotions and sweats - I was just about holding onto my identity.

Then my hair started to get noticeably thinner and I thought, 'Thanks a lot. Now I'm not a woman any more, even my hair's starting to act like a man's!' It hasn't all fallen out, it just seems to get thinner year by year. I hate having to go to the hairdresser so often to get it styled; it makes me feel like a senior, and I'm years away from that. Minoxidil did not work well enough for me."

What is harder to handle is the double blow to a feminine image when head and pubic hair thin, while facial hair thickens and darkens. But health professionals observe that most women find thinning hair less troubling than the other menopausal changes such as mood swings.

Hair Loss and Youth

When pre-school children lose hair, the significance is minor. At school, however, the desire to identify with others makes them sensitive to reactions. At best, there is sympathy and curiosity; at worst, relentless cruelty. Whatever the response, a child with less hair has more attention than is wanted. They may respond by withdrawing into a silence fostered by depression or isolation. They may put up with jibes in a mature way, learning an early lesson in how to deal with hostility. Occasionally they become loud and 'bratty', covering up inner anger or insecurity. If the child's struggle for acceptance isn't aided by parents or school staff, they may try moving desperately from school to school, hoping to keep their stigma hidden at the next. But all that follows is that the child never has time enough to build close friendships with classmates who might prove allies. One older woman with alopecia totalis never finished high school because of the struggle, which was aggravated by the fact that "they didn't make wigs made for youngsters in those days."

Losing hair isn't fair: it upsets a child's natural sense of justice. It isn't their fault they lost their hair and they need to know this, especially if classmates imply the opposite. Time seems to run slower when young, so suffering can seem everlasting. Trying to live in the present rather than imagining a hopeless future can help. Children have a need to cry out some of the trauma and bitterness, and to use the emotionally healing gift of humour. Being taught to be proud of themselves and see their 'difference' in perspective increases self-confidence, which acts as a defence against being picked on. Reading matter that touches on physical difference or loss can also help; E. Nesbit's *Melisande* is a fairytale featuring a bald princess.

Many alopecians do extremely well at sports or academic subjects. If they are overcompensating, assuming that they have to work twice as hard to prove their worth or to avoid teasing, children may need to explore the pressures they live with.

Finding time to ask children about their emotions, friends, problems and dreams can help them work out what hair loss really means for them. This can lead on to specific problem-solving, and helping identify different ways of coping so they don't feel their back is against the wall. When adults show by their actions and words that they accept and love their 'ugly duckling,' that duckling is encouraged to blossom into a swan.

Cherokee Indian

_____

Chapter 7

TOO LITTLE HAIR,
TOO MANY FEELINGS

"The weight of this sad time we must obey;
Speak what we feel, not what we ought to say."

Shakespeare, *King Lear*

FEELINGS

Hair loss can be accompanied by feeling:		
★ confused	★ devastated	★ depressed
★ 'bad'	★ guilty	★ ashamed
★ bitter	★ resentful	★ angry
★ humiliated	★ powerless	★ unacceptable
★ isolated	★ frustrated	★ hopeless
★ despairing	★ disillusioned	★ terrified
★ embarrassed	★ betrayed	★ anxious

Help! I've got Feelings!

Every day we undergo myriads of feelings, yet in general the white Anglo-Saxon majority culture in North America is remarkably uncomfortable with most emotions; the strongest ones, love and anger, when modified as sex and violence, form the big attractions of the adult film world. We have inherited a stiff upper lip mentality which is long on action and talk, and short on expressing emotions, particularly the 'softer' ones such as tenderness, compassion and vulnerability.

There are variations, of course: men and the middle class face more restrictions on expressing feelings than do women and the working class. Other cultures expect emotions to be expressed in everyday life: Italian and Arab men touch each other in affection, cry if they are sad, and shout and gesticulate if they are angry.

> What's invisible, can't be given away and can overwhelm even the strongest? A Feeling

In comparison, North Americans are uncertain beginners at emotional skills. Nobody is *forced* to deal with feelings, of course, but avoiding them can have dire consequences on mental and physical well-being. In the popular TV show *Babes* Wendy Jo Sperber called anger "the cholesterol of the soul." Keeping feelings caged up inside leaves them to maul us internally. Ulcers, migraines, eczema and alcohol/drug addiction, have been linked with repressed emotions. Imagining that emotions aren't real or important hinders progress through the stages of grief towards adjustment - and being able to get on with the rest of life. If we delay work on feelings, adapting to hair loss can drag on indefinitely, despite the impression that a calm exterior suggests we are coping admirably. A trucker in his mid thirties with androgenetic alopecia comments:

> "After my hair started falling out I must have spent a couple of years feeling kind of bad inside. I was thinking all the fun was over, I was past it now and what's the point? I just started drinking more and more, and that made me think I was really crummy.

If anyone joked about 'chrome dome' or that kind of s---, I pretended it didn't get to me. But if I was drunk I could get aggressive.

"When my brother came to visit one summer he said I had to pull myself together and stop picking on people. So I talked about it with him, how things really were. And it helped. I got into AA and I started to open up a bit, but there's still a long way to go."

Social norms require that we express strong emotions in safe situations - not in places like church or the office. Outside a private place, the safest way to express fear or anger is indirectly, through humour, irritation or sulking. But these everyday safety valves are inadequate for the flood of emotions hair loss can produce. When feelings aren't expressed, they sneak out in some other behaviour pattern, such as:

- soldiering on (being brave and self-sacrificing)

- repetitive complaining

- withdrawal

- bitterness

- self-blame.

The consequences of thinking that the material world - money, work, food - is more important than emotions can seriously affect those around you, too. Psychologist Alice Miller claims that it's not trauma that's hard to deal with, but the effects of not processing the distress.

Dealing with Feelings

The majority culture classifies emotions as 'positive' (joy, love) or 'negative' (anger, despair). This misleadingly suggests that negative emotions are somehow bad or unforgivable. But feelings spring up as naturally as grass; we have control not over their existence but over what we do with the ones we have.

Looking bravely and honestly at your emotions is the key to overcoming the trauma of hair loss. It's the gateway to learning to love and accept yourself as you are. It's hard to believe at first, but the pain will pass. A young trainee therapist with male pattern baldness compared hair loss to a tree:

"A tree can't just produce beautiful flowers - you have to get down in the dirt, rocks, bugs and all, to put down roots. *Then* you'll be able to flower."

There are four essential tasks:

1. **Name (Acknowledge)**

Learn to listen to your body and mind for clues about what you are feeling - the shakiness of fear in the stomach, or the tight jaw of anger. Admit to yourself, "Right now, I am afraid. It's fine to be afraid, it's perfectly logical and understandable."

2. **Feel**

Focus on the physical sensation of the emotion, allow your mind to come up with the thoughts that accompany the feeling. Look with curiosity at this feeling. They're called 'feelings' because you are supposed to *feel* them, not stamp on them.

3. **Express**

Writing about your feelings can be a therapeutic and safe way of expressing them; or tell a trusted friend, or paint angrily, or dance or stamp your feet. One woman with alopecia areata created a huge collage to express her overwhelming anger and despair. A busy Montreal journalist and mother discovered she could yell to her heart's content while driving with her windows rolled shut. Some friends and I released plenty of anger and frustration by shouting "NO!" into a howling gale on top of a Cornish cliff. Use your imagination.

4. Forgive Yourself

Recognize that feelings are an aspect of humanity to be thankful for. Life is colourless without them. You are human and vulnerable - that is a real strength. Tell yourself aloud, "I have a right to be in despair (or angry, or whatever), and I forgive myself."

These steps help bring feelings into the light of day where they can lose their destructive power by fading away.

Destructive Beliefs About Ourselves

External and internal pressures can seriously complicate the life of a silkhead. Your boss telling you that you must wear a wig to work is external pressure, as is being teased or attacked by classmates. Internal pressure is when you believe that the external messages about being unacceptable or ugly are true.

Negative messages from those we relate to or the society in which we live hook into any shaky feelings we already have about ourselves, reinforcing them so we end up accepting and believing those damning judgements.

The Big Picture

One way to keep from being hard on yourself and to get things into perspective is to think about *others* who have lost their hair: would you think

Hall of Fame

ROY CASTLE, British entertainer, appeared on Rolf Harris' TV show Cartoon Club while hairless from chemotherapy. He was delighted at being sketched by Harris during the program.

them useless to themselves or society? Think of the achieve-ments of Mikhail Gorbachev, Telly Savalas, and the Silkhead Hall of Fame roster. Are people with cancer unworthy of love and success? Are they useless because they found chemotherapy tough going? Are children with alopecia areata ugly and unlovable? If not, why think this way about *yourself?* Charity begins at home: for many, the most difficult person to be good to is oneself.

When very young children lose hair, they don't believe that being hairless makes them inferior or ugly. They're more likely not to dwell on it, or to think of it as an inter-esting difference, like having an unusual toy. The chil-dren's friends might be curious but not judgmental. Only later are children influenced by the surrounding propa-ganda about hair loss - sometimes, unfortunately, because parents or teachers have conveyed disapproval or rejec-tion.

Like animals, we are born with complete self-accept-ance. But countless, often unpredictable forces act upon us throughout our lives. Some people and events reinforce

our concept of ourselves as just fine, but others negate this. Somewhere along the line, these out-side criticisms be-come an 'inner critic' (some call it the Censor or Thought Police).

Losing hair can give this damning inner

voice so much ammunition that we can be crushed or devastated by it. Devastate - from the Latin to lay waste - was
what armies did to thriving towns. They killed everyone
and everything, destroyed all the buildings and crops, and
left the place a wasteland.

Affirmations

Freeing yourself from the inner put-downs isn't easy:
we can't remove the part of the mind that has been brain-
washed into low self-esteem. One alternative is to bom-
bard yourself with repeated positive messages, called *affirmations*.

The messages need be nothing more than the exact opposite of the internal critic's complaints.

Using Affirmations

Using affirmations is standard practice in psychotherapy
and in self-help approaches to issues as diverse as shy-
ness, goal-setting and cancer. Getting into a relaxed state
first, e.g. through hypnosis, meditation or muscle-by-mus-
cle relaxation is most effective; then repeat the affirmations.
It is particularly powerful to record your own voice on a
cassette and play it back; this seems to confuse the inner
critic.

What worked well for me was writing my affirmations
on a small card. Most mornings I would repeat them a few
times. I carried the card in my wallet so that whenever I
had a few spare moments - in my lunch break, on the bus,
waiting in line - I could reread it. Over time it really made
me think differently about myself and my hair loss.

The best affirmations for me were:

1. "There's nothing wrong with me!"

Having a medical condition doesn't mean there's something wrong with my personality, with me *as a person*.

This affirmation also reminds me that I am far more than just a hair loss victim.

2. "I am fully human and wonderful to be close to. I am a fine friend/partner/daughter etc."

It took months of repetition before I could really believe this, but the message has seeped in now.

However positively you cope with hair loss, there will be occasions when you are sad or overwhelmed - just as in life before the Big Fall. Using affirmations, those periods of the blues lift quicker. Affirmations don't have to be repeated for the rest of your life: confidence, hope and happiness don't vanish if you tail off. You may need only

---

Whispers From The Inner Critic...

"I look like an alien."

"I feel like a freak."

"No one can find a man [woman] without hair sexy."

"I'm so ugly."

"How can my wife and children say they still love me?"

"If people knew I had no hair my life would be hell."

"There's something wrong with me."

"It must be my fault in some way."

"I *ought* to be able to cope with this."

"Only beautiful people deserve love and success."

"Having an illness is an unfair burden on others."

"This proves I'm useless, just as I always knew, deep down."

"There isn't enough love to go round - I guess it'll go to people who are normal and look good."

---

an infrequent top up; if you like the effect, find or create other affirmations to take you to new places.

A Word of Warning

Some affirmations may be difficult to say. You may find, as I did, that when you say them, you start to feel intense emotions such as anger, despair or panic. This is because saying "NO!" to your inner critic contradicts attitudes that have been planted strong and deep. If you find you need it, allow yourself privacy and time to recover.

I spent the first several months after all my hair fell out hoping that someone would rescue me. A doctor, my partner Tom, some miracle... then I discovered an alopecia network. And it didn't rescue me, either. I was forced, in

---

Affirmations: The Reality Is...

"I am human and deserve to be treated that way."

"I am perfectly normal and acceptable."

"Sexiness is an attitude, not a hairstyle"

"I look different; I also look really good."

"If my wife and kids say they love me, I'd better believe them."

"I may be bald but I still deserve a full and happy life.

"There's nothing wrong with me."

"I'm not to blame for my hair loss or for feeling bad about it."

"I'm doing fine in a difficult situation."

"Everybody deserves an equal opportunity for love and success."

"Being ill is bad luck, but not my fault; others are lucky it hasn't happened to them."

"Here's my chance to prove I'm much stronger and more capable than I ever thought."

"There is far more love in the world than we ever tap into. I'm going to plunge into being loved, head first!"

---

the end, to do my own work: no one else could wave that magic wand to make me feel better. I've had to learn how to build up my confidence, how to ask for help and support, and how to break through the shell that alopecia trapped me in. I've had to learn to let in the love of others, and go to support groups even when I felt like hiding, fearful that I might break down. I discovered that the more anxious I stayed, the more uncomfortable or upset this made those around me. This motivated me to come to terms with alopecia more quickly.

Most of the emotions we go through are common to anyone who suffers a major loss. However well prepared we are, the reality of hair loss still stuns. It takes grieving to 'process' the loss.

LOSS AND GRIEF

Losing More than Hair

Additional losses can include:

★ laughter	★ happiness	★ trust
★ desire	★ power	★ compassion
★ love	★ work	★ play
★ friends	★ focus	★ money
★ confidence	★ identity	★ boldness

Identity Change

Loss accompanies all major life changes, however positive they appear. If we marry, we lose that old single person we are so familiar with. When we graduate, we lose the framework and direction that school provides. Such transitions, the death of an old aspect and birth of a new, are a good time to reflect on who or what is the *real* you. Just last year, for example, four years after my hair fell out, I realized that this loss had revealed the long-buried introverted 'little Sheila'; she had disappeared under the more extrovert personality I thought I needed in order to be an adult.

Cancer often involves the loss of some body part through surgery, which may overshadow any other change. But hair loss is a *real* loss, a loss of part of our identity, producing feelings that are difficult or painful to face - just like the death of a loved one, or the end of a relationship. John Bowlby, author of three books on separation and loss, observes that people often underestimate how "intensely distressing and disabling" loss is.

In a world where people daily ask "How are you?" but don't wait for an answer, it can be hard to acknowledge our grief. We feel as though we're giving in to negativity, living in the past, wallowing in our own pain. We're not exactly fun to be around. There's no doubt, too, that grieving is tiring - emotionally and even physically draining. But to deny painful feelings in favour of forced positivity does not work; we can't 'let go' of anger until we have grasped it. Looking at anger and despair is not giving up hope but dealing with the present, with the emotions that are there right now. Grieving is a project that you *must* devote time to if you want to adapt to hair loss. Unless we allow ourselves to recall in full what has been lost, and mourn it, we limp into the future with this 'unfinished business' like a weight still tied to our legs.

One of the most difficult aspects of hair loss is that you can't hurry healing. I wanted to get back on track with the life I had planned, so my impatience made me angry. But like the vegetables I grow, I had to allow my adjustment to take its own time.

Commenting on the common reluctance to grieve, Betty Jane Wylie quotes Rabbi Earl Grollman, "Grief is an emotion, not a disease." *(New Beginnings: Living Through Loss and Grief)*. It is also a process of transformation. People who persevere in dealing with grief are often recreated, as if they are their old selves but with an extra dimension of maturity. They create new ways of responding to difficulties, and instead of seeing life through the blurred tearstains of unhappiness or the shakiness of anxiety, the world appears clear, fresh and stimulating.

Grieving

Cancer professionals are experienced in the grieving process. They know its importance and have contributed enormously to research and practice in this area. Dr. Elisabeth Kubler-Ross, a psychiatrist who has worked for years with the terminally ill, was the first to analyze the stages of adapting to loss as:

Denial

Depression

Bargaining

Anger

Acceptance

Other therapists have revised these stages, but the five above are generally accepted. They provide a very useful way of making sense of what happens when hair is lost and guidelines for working through the experience. Individuals usually experience shock at sudden loss and may go through the stages in any order, moving back and forth between them. It's not necessarily a clear progression.

The more sudden and dramatic the loss, the stronger

the emotions. For men and women who lose hair through the usually gradual process of androgenetic alopecia, emotions may be spread out and not as intense. They may not even notice the change. Some, however, experience a 'crunch,' often provoked by a remark or chance glimpse of the thinning or bald spot from a new angle. One sales executive relates:

"It was a terrific shock. I was twenty seven, and I was looking in the mirror at a friend's; she had one of these three-way mirrors. I saw this white patch at the back of my head. At first I thought there was something wrong. Nobody had ever told me I was going bald, not a single person."

Denial

"This can't be happening to me"

"I must just be moulting a bit - it's spring, isn't it?"

"I'm too young"

"I don't like it but I don't have a problem with it"

These are the sort of thoughts that arise on noticing hair falling. Shock and numbness set in; panic often follows. Denial is a response to major change and may conceal terror about the future. Fear is something that affects many hair loss sufferers, especially those with cancer or alopecia areata, since the disease may strike again.

When mine began to drop out in quantity, I was confused. I wondered whether I was just imagining it. When I finally had to admit that something abnormal was going on, I still thought it would stop very soon. I couldn't believe that *all* of it would fall out, until most of it had gone.

Working it through

Alopecians can hardly deny the facts which stare them

in the face. Denial can take the form of avoiding all mirrors, a reluctance to tell anyone about the hair loss, or a denial of the truth: "I'm just fine." Concealment can permit the pretence that there is no loss. This doesn't mean that anyone who wears a wig is 'in denial.' Most of us wear wigs, scarves or hats in some circumstances, and there are people who wear wigs constantly but look at their uncovered head in the mirror quite happily, and have told their social circle that they wear a wig.

A dentist friend who developed cancer in his thirties illustrates another way denial works. After the worst of the chemotherapy was over, I saw him at a dinner party. I wondered how hair loss had affected him, especially as he was wearing a winter hat, furry earflaps and all, at the table. "Oh no, I don't have any problems about losing hair," he told me. Yet now his hair is back and the hat is off, he is free to admit the pain he was denying at the time. It's safe to talk about trauma when it's over.

A classic denial from Ronald Reagan is reported in Susan Sontag's *AIDS and its Metaphors:*

> "When asked how he felt after his cancer operation, he declared, 'I didn't have cancer. I had something inside of me that had cancer in it and it was removed.'"

Initially, acknowledging the reality of the new you can bring out overwhelming emotions. This can jolt you into another stage, as can being exposed in front of other people. Now is the time to admit that you can't deal with this on your own and must find help. It may be as simple as talking to just one person about what you are going through.

Rushing the denial stage is not useful. Don't let people label you 'in denial' and try to push you out of it; the stage is essential. Saying "No!" shows a healthy sense of self.

Bargaining

"Please let my hair grow back, God - I'll go to church every Sunday and act a better Christian, if you do."

"If I try every possible treatment, it has to grow back."

"If my hair grows back I'll give up cigarettes."

Bargaining is a private train of thought whose significance is not always understood. It is a last ditch attempt to hold onto hope. I made a deal with myself that I would do everything possible to lower my stress, and this would return my hair. The deal didn't work, thus propelling me to the next stages, anger and depression. Bargaining is not a stage that 'succeeds,' but is a step on the ladder we have to climb to get out of the pits. It shows us the limit of our control over loss.

Working it through

Notice when you begin to bargain. If you can accept the bargain is unlikely to work, it is possible to concentrate on the other stages. But most need to bargain and believe that it might work. Miracles can happen; with alopecia areata and cancer, remissions do occur. Be prepared, however, for a drop into anger or depression if it becomes clear that while you have kept your side of the bargain, the results you hoped for haven't materialized.

Anger

"I hate myself. I'm the ugliest thing in the world."

"It's all your fault - it would never have happened if you had treated me better"

"I'll never trust a doctor again. They don't know anything."

"Why me? I don't deserve this!"

Women, pressured to be 'nice,' often turn fear or anger

119

inwards, which becomes general depression or anxiety. In contrast men, raised not to admit feelings, often turn their depression, fear or turmoil outwards, into anger. In other words, the same psychological state may pitch one alopecian into anger, another into depression.

Some people find anger the most difficult stage, especially if those around them suggest they are being unreasonable. It is seldom possible to find anyone or anything to blame for what seems like unjust punishment. Dylan Thomas knew this anger well when he wrote at his father's blindness and impending death:

"Do not go gentle into that good night,
Rage, rage against the dying of the light."

After the initial shock of losing my hair wore off I was howlingly angry. I was angry with myself, my partner, the medical establishment for not having a cure, and angry with every single person who had hair. I was angry with everyone, whether they sympathized, mocked, or ignored my hair loss. Anger is valuable because it is such a powerful, outward-directed emotion. It makes up for the flip side of hair loss, of feeling a powerless victim. Anger gives us a sense of power and control, and provides energy that can catapult us out of withdrawal, denial or depression, towards change.

Working it through

There is a difference between *feeling* anger and *acting* on it. This is especially important if you find yourself directing anger towards an inappropriate target, such as the person helping you select a wig. You can welcome it as a stage in resolving loss but letting rip at your nearest and dearest, or yourself, is counter-productive. There are many ways of expressing anger in a non-harmful way: stamping, yelling loudly, punching a mattress or cushion, throwing rocks into the ocean, smashing cheap plates in a safe place, or doing some vigorous sports such as tennis or running. The important thing is to do any one of these with *all* your energy until you're exhausted.

When anger is repressed it can show itself in depression or habits that are destructive to oneself such as:

- nail-biting, lip-chewing, 'slashing'

- anorexia, bulimia (or simple overeating), addictions such as overwork, overspending, alcohol, drugs

- general lack of self-care, irritability, social isolation

- sleeping irregularities, ill-health, suicide wishes

- difficulty in concentrating

Depression

"I can't live like this."

"I might as well give up."

"I don't feel up to going to work today."

"Just leave me alone. It's all hopeless."

"There's no point in trying a support group - everyone else will know each other anyway."

Psychologists know that depression is not meaningless pain or self-indulgence but a healing process. Swedish psychoanalyst Emmy Gut in her book *Productive and Unproductive Depression* suggests depression often *enables* people to resolve major impasses in life. It may be the only way to isolate yourself from outside pressures in order to grieve and rethink your life.

Depression literally means a weighting down. It is a withdrawal from the outside world into a mental pain-room. Despair, its cousin, means a loss of hope. The loss of hope is a direct result of realizing that the bargain has failed, or that you can no longer deny what is happening.

It's connected with the lack of power over hair loss. When we realize nothing can be done to make it regrow we realize we can't control and plan our lives the way our technology-based culture suggests. Nor can we place blind faith in medicine and ignore or abuse our bodies. There is a sense of isolation in this new game. The well-worn paths have disappeared and we have to hack through unknown territory.

Depression arises from feeling powerless, and from social pressures clashing with personal needs or situations. Almost everyone who is fearful about how hair loss will affect their lives, or who is disturbed at their change in appearance, becomes depressed. When you think all your plans, activities, abilities are ruined, life seems to lose its purpose. What point is there in going out... getting dressed... getting up... eating?

No attempts to cheer me up worked. I didn't want to see anyone or leave the house, although I went to work when it was essential. I couldn't stop crying. When my hair disappeared I wanted to die. The depression lessened as I began to exercise more control over the situation by gradually letting others in on my 'secret'. Depression returns occasionally, usually caused by something other than hair loss.

Working it through

Hiding away to 'lick one's wounds' is as natural for humans as for animals. Psychological wounds aren't imaginary. Allow yourself to hide, and particulary to cry. Tears eliminate body toxins; they act as a healing flushing system, so the more you cry, the less toxins and hopelessness remain bottled up inside.

But a balance must be struck between isolation and social mixing, otherwise depression can skew your thinking. If, as I did, you feel unable to talk with friends, even over the phone, sending them a note from the edge of your personal precipice will remind you that you *do* have people who care about you. Staying in touch is a stepping stone for the time you want people back in your life. It is certainly essential to have someone - partner, parent, doctor, friend - check on you at intervals to act as buoys steering you clear of the rocks. If you have suicidal thoughts, see a physician or mental health professional immediately for support.

Even if it's the last thing you want, doing something practical periodically such as cooking a meal will keep you in contact with what was once your normal routine, ready for the time when, believe it or not, you will be able to recover your life and happiness.

Acceptance

Acceptance of the new situation doesn't mean the trauma is erased as though it never happened. The scars remain and will ache at times. You have done your best with that experience and can go on to others. Adapting is not a static, happy-ever-after state: it is the ability and skill to juggle, to keep your balance on a swaying ship. It's learning how to respond flexibly to future changes and demands, a skill every silkhead gets plenty of practice in. After hair loss, you will never be the same again. But then, isn't that true of every change in life? Out of the ashes of the old you rises the new, clean, transformed self.

Going through the process yourself affects those around you while they too are experiencing some of the stages of grief over the loss of the old you. This is why your loved ones might refuse to speak of what is happening, cry or become hostile, responses that can confuse new alopecians.

There are excellent books about loss, many of which relate to cancer and address the ultimate loss, death. Those undergoing chemotherapy or radiation may find that loss

123

of hair pales in comparison with the loss of health, dignity, and a relatively pain-free, worry-free life. A teacher in her fifties commented:

> "Considering what I've been through with cancer - all these major changes that have led me to question my values and do a lot of soul-searching while sick - losing my hair for a while didn't seem that big a deal."

Some, however, are surprised by the strength of their grief:

> "Chemo puts you through it all. With surgery and chemo, it seemed my body wasn't mine any more, it was very hard to keep hold of any sense of self-respect. And then when your hair goes as well, it just seems the last straw, even though I thought I shouldn't be so vain. I felt destroyed."

In *New Beginnings,* Betty Jane Wylie notes "self-protective isolation is almost automatic and certainly necessary." Although she is writing primarily about the loss of a spouse, her suggestion of spending time alone to cry and giving yourself lots of tender loving care is something new silkheads definitely need. The tendency is to be hard on yourself, and to go on a wild search for cures. Taking time to reflect, to cry out some of that grief and fear, is a *healthy* response. It's admitting that a demanding change is in progress. As Audre Lord writes:

> "Caring for myself is not self-indulgence, it's self-preservation."

HEALING

"Two heads are better than one"

"A trouble shared is a trouble halved"

Why?

Many people have described both cancer and alopecia areata as 'emotional roller-coasters,' and you can't think straight when you're on one of those. You need stability, and feedback from someone else. In particular, if the underlying problem is the conviction that less hair makes you a lesser person, only by voicing your experiences and fears can you learn that you are wrong. Support groups can help, but if there are many people contending for limited time, you may not get much beyond telling your story, and healing demands more.

Getting good listening is not the same as talking about your worries with someone who may interrupt, comment, tell you what to do, or listen with just half an ear. Trained counsellors or therapists can listen and encourage you to recover a sense of normality. A counsellor's role is not to advise but to listen with respect, attention and acceptance.

Yet just at the time we really need it, we sometimes

Look After Yourself With:

☆ gentle happy music ☆ your favourite food

☆ long relaxing baths ☆ a massage or sauna

☆ a holiday ☆ a walk in nature

☆ another holiday!

☆ physical activity e.g. sport or a swim

☆ flowers or plants for the house or garden

☆ a day in a library or gallery or somewhere new

☆ buy something you've wanted for a long time: a new tool or book

Make your own list and stick it on the fridge door

---

avoid asking for help. The majority culture is no longer geared to the co-operation and mutual help found in smaller, less 'progressive' cultures or previous centuries. Independence, in the sense of bravely suffering in isolation, is not a sign of maturity; *inter*dependence is. By depending on others, offering or accepting a helping hand, we work wonders.

A decade ago conventional wisdom was that sick people needed experts. Now, though, people are much more aware of psychology and its key concepts. Many have had some sort of 'personal development' experience, whether it's assertiveness, confidence-building or family therapy. People know much more about counselling, because listening skills are now valued in so many types of work, from teaching through marketing to management.

There are two options for healing - a professional therapist, or finding an active listener (confidante). I was lucky enough to have free professional psychotherapy (through medical referral in the British healthcare system) and peer counselling through the co-counselling network I had been trained in. I would recommend that anyone who can, should get as much 'listening' of whatever type as they can.

Professional therapists may cost, but many offer a sliding scale of fees. They are experienced in dealing with people in crisis. Peer ('amateur') counselling is free and many non-therapists (e.g. voluntary workers or church leaders) have been trained in counselling skills. Some cancer survivors train as volunteer counsellors to aid current sufferers (the Cansurmount program is an example). Therapy allows you to be an active participant in your own emotional healing, which is very powerful if you have felt a helpless victim.

Choosing a Non-Professional

Think carefully about the possibilities. The person you're closest to may not be the best; my feelings towards my partner Tom were too mixed, he seemed too involved in the trauma. My best friend was too busy to commit herself to regular sessions. Some people I knew were too down themselves, or too talkative. I chose one of my co-counsellors, Janet: she lived close by, had suffered loss herself, and wasn't someone I saw socially. I felt safe to disclose to her how I *really* felt.

If no money is changing hands, I like the idea of barter. Janet would counsel me for thirty minutes then I would do the same for her. Other exchanges are possible: flowers, home produce, a meal, or doing work such as childminding or financial advice - whatever you can offer. This has the added benefit of reminding you that hair or no, you are a useful, worthwhile person.

When looking for a professional or amateur counsellor, use the checklist opposite. Interview a few potential helpers before you commit yourself. If you find more than one, use them.

STEPS IN HEALING

How to Start

Prepare your counsellor for the special situation and issues of hair loss by asking them to read background literature (e.g. brochures about alopecia areata) or this book - at least chapter 6. (If they are non-professionals they might read other material about grieving or counselling.) The more information, the better prepared they will be. Work out how often to meet; find a place and time when you will not be interrupted.

The perfect place to counsel is a room (or wide open

Who to Choose?

- a counsellor/therapist who deals with grief and loss issues
- a trusted relative who is not too affected personally
- a cleric or spiritual guide
- a social worker or other trained counsellor
- a sympathetic GP may make time to give you a series of counselling appointments
- a friend or work colleague - not necessarily the one you are closest to
- a support group member, if they are not too close to their own trauma to be detached
- a school counsellor or sympathetic teacher/tutor

Qualities to Look For

- able to keep confidences - who won't talk to others about your 'session'
- good listener
- not upset at the way you look, not prejudiced
- mature enough to allow - even encourage - you to cry, be angry (perhaps someone who has weathered a loss themselves)
- likes you and wants to help

Attitudes Checklist

Avoid people who might think:
- "Hair loss is nothing compared to real loss"
- "It's vain [or unmanly] to worry about your appearance"
- "We deserve what we get"
- "A woman's appearance is her biggest asset"
- "Hair loss is a complete tragedy"
- "You can heal yourself of anything"

space) where you can make as much noise as you want. Yelling or growling into a cushion (and pounding it) can be a good compromise.

Stages of Counselling

Tell your story

Use as much detail as possible - every little thing *is* important. When feelings arise, let your counsellor know, and allow yourself to express them, through crying, yelling, shaking laughing, yawning: this is the healing process. Then carry on with your story.

People often need to tell their story a few times. (Have you noticed how some people will repeat some incident to several friends in turn before they have fully 'processed' it and can move on to talk of other matters?)

There are always more tears, anger etc. inside. You can get in touch with these by having your counsellor say affirmations to you. The quickest way to emotional discharge is for you to say them to your counsellor.

Get a reality check

Get your counsellor to remind you:

- You're *not* alone: there are millions of people with cancer and alopecia areata and thinning hair in North America alone.

- You did not cause this trauma.

- You *will* adjust to it some day; you have come so far already.

- You have your counsellor and others who still love *you*, not the missing hair.

- You are a unique and valuable person.

Think about support

What are your needs right now, and how can you meet them? What gets in the way? What goals can you set and plan for?

Accept your appearance

'Unveil' in front of your counsellor. Let your feelings emerge. The most powerful experience for most silkheads is to look in a mirror with a supportive friend. I couldn't believe it when Janet suggested I do this - I even got angry with her. She kept her cool, and I dissolved into tears just at the thought of it. Eventually I tried it. She put her arm round me, and I was able to express a lot more grief.

Roleplay

How to tell others about your hair loss; how to uncover if you want to; how to deal with hostile or unsympathetic responses. Nobody is *required* to tell anyone about their hair loss - or uncover - but discussing such steps is an essential step in moving out of the denial stage in order to release the fear that holds so many of us back. For some, just talking about such a step is all they need to clear that hurdle of shame or humiliation.

Self-Validation

Boast about yourself to your counsellor! Many groups that work on shame use the concept of the Inner Child or the 'Real Sheila Jacobs.' I find encouraging clients to tell me all that's good about themselves, at length, helps them get in touch with their *real* self. It is another 'reality check', and raises self-esteem.

At the end of a session, you need to move from your inner emotional world to the outer world. Tell your confidante about some event or activity you are looking forward to, or get them to ask you general knowledge questions or puzzles.

Ways To Build Confidence

One of the best ways to cope with hair loss is to contact others in the same boat. Just meeting one other person who wears a wig, for example, counteracts that sense of isolation.

Newsletters can be a lifeline for those who live far from support groups. The kind of information and advice they cover might include prostheses (such as wigs); emotional coping strategies; book reviews; the legal position on employment rights; campaigns for better medical insurance. In addition, through newsletters people can find penpals, other silkheads who live close by - and even humour to lighten the load. Organizations such as the National Coalition for Cancer Survivorship, the Bald Headed Men of America, the National Alopecia Areata Foundation and the Canadian Alopecia Areata Association all send newsletters to members and hire out videos on hair loss.

Support groups (often affiliated to these organizations) can be found in most major cities in North America. If there isn't one for your type of hair loss, it may be worth attending another as so many of the issues are similar. Cancer clinics and agencies often run support groups, sometimes a different one for each type of cancer. The British Columbia Cancer Agency, for example, currently runs separate groups for breast cancer, brain cancer and prostate cancer.

A recent study reports that women with breast cancer who attended a support group lived on average an astonishing 18 months longer than those who stayed isolated. Not only does sociability increase health, laughter does too, and one good way to bring laughter into your life is to go to a support group. Norman Cousins *(Head First)* reports a great deal of research into the effect of laughter: typical benefits are increased creativity, flexibility, ability to withstand tension and physical discomfort, as well as lower cortisone (immune-suppressant) levels.

Each support group differs. Some are run on the Twelve

SNAPPY COMEBACKS TO SILLY COMMENTS
Embarrassment can cause people to make the silliest comments. For those days when you're too busy or tired to explain - or when you've heard that 'joke' for the sixth time that day - here are a few snappy comebacks.

Q: You've got no hair!
A: Oh dear, I must have left it somewhere. Now was it the bank or the supermarket?
Q: Have you lost your hair?
A: Yes, very observant of you. I lost it at a poker game last night.
Q: Can I touch your head?
A: Yes, but I charge $5 a touch.
Q: How did you lose your hair?
A: People kept wanting to touch it, and it gradually wore away.
Q: You'd better be careful in the sun.
A: Luckily my brain didn't fall out along with my hair - I bought some sunscreen.
Q: Why have you shaved your head?
A: So I can get to talk to people [morons] like you.
A: For a bet.
A: To be cool.
A: For charity.
A: It's a political protest. I sent all the shavings to President Bush along with a photo of the new me, to condemn the cuts *he* has made.
Q: Don't you get cold?
A: Fortunately I've discovered these wonderful things called hats.

Q: Hey, baldy!

A: Yes, shaggy?

Q: Willya look at that!

A: Wanna join my fan club?

A: Jealous? I'll let you in on my secret - for a price...

Q: Hey, chrome dome, get a rug!

A: Hey, tunnelmouth, get a muzzle!

Q: I know where you can go to get something done about your hair.

A: What hair? *This* is a wig!

A: What makes you think I want to look like you?

Q: Have you got cancer?

A: Have you got a problem with how other people look?

Q: Wouldn't you feel more comfortable with a hairpiece?

A: I'd feel more comfortable if people could accept I like how I look.

Q: I heard this really great joke about baldness the other day.

A: Great. Go tell it to someone who cares, like your mother.

Q: Is that your own hair?

A: No, it's my grandfather's - he left it to me in his will. Would you like to try it on?

Q: Is that a wig?

A: No, it's a banana. What's wrong with your eyes?

Q: I can tell you're wearing a wig. What have you got?

A: I've got better things to do with my time than answer inane questions.

Step (Alcoholics Anonymous) model, some will be more flexible and informal, others still may focus on expert speakers and fund-raising for medical research. Some are run by members, others by medical personnel, social workers or psychologists. But the burning issues in many groups are common:
- cosmetic issues (e.g. how to care for wigs or use make up to camouflage a lack of eyebrows or lashes)
- medical research (and 'alternative' treatments)
- campaigning for better medical insurance in your state or province
- discussing how to cope with every type of emotional problem

Another benefit of support groups is not the support you get but what you can offer. Finding your experience can help others like you can dramatically raise your feelings of self-worth. *We* are experts on how to cope.

The annual conferences held by some of the organizations above are even more useful in restoring a sense of normality. I have attended two NAAF conferences and found that to be surrounded by 300-odd silkheads is heaven. You are no longer in a minority, and can socialize without any anxious undercurrents. This experience can transform how you feel about hair loss.

Allow yourself to dream and to hope. Think about the challenge of hair loss and how your values are changing. Loss is like being on one set of tracks when the points are switched. Suddenly you're on an unplanned journey; an exciting mystery tour lies ahead, if you can open your mind to change and enjoy it.

Other Ways to Build Confidence

1. Go to a self-esteem or confidence-building course.

2. Assertiveness training focuses on techniques for dealing with other people confidently.

3. Regular physical exercise can increase confidence and lower stress, especially if done with one or more others.

4. The number of books (and now videos) on self-esteem has snowballed since Dale Carnegie wrote *How to Win Friends and Influence People* back in 1936. Check the popular psychology section of your library or bookstore.

5. Taking small risks can increase confidence by increasing your sense of personal power and capability (e.g. casually mentioning your illness if the opportunity arises, rather than avoiding it).

6. Setting achievable goals and working towards them also helps increase the sense of our own abilities. Doing so in a group, with feedback and encouragement, makes it twice as effective.

7. Keep a daily list or journal of what you have achieved that day. Read it before bed.

8. Learn from children: be frivolous and crazy, get as much fun and laughter as possible.

9. If your life seems like a prison sentence, work out how to make it more of an adventure.

10. Find ways of offering love to others.

Baldness in Popular Culture

Long before Sinead O'Connor shaved her head and shot to fame, alopecians featured in popular culture. Back in the 1940s blues musician Eddie 'Cleanhead' Vinson penned a song lamenting that he'd been jilted because of his lack of hair. Hairless comic heroes include Charles Xavier of the X-Men, Yang, and Moondragon, a bald heroine. The much-loved film creatures ET and Yoda (Star Wars), as well as the demand for Cabbage Patch dolls, show that hair isn't a prerequisite for popularity. T shirts spotted include:

> **Hall of Fame**
>
> DUNCAN GOODHEW was called 'Baldilocks' at school when he developed alopecia areata, but went on to become a champion swimmer. After winning a gold medal for Britain in the 1980 Olympics, he is now a TV presenter. "There are very few negative things that occur to me about being bald."

- *Hair today? Gone tomorrow*
- *From hair to here*
- *This isn't a bald spot, it's a solar panel for a sex machine*

- *The Lord is just, the Lord is fair*
  He gave some brains, the others hair
  (John Capps)

How about:

- *Clean up the environment - get rid of your hair*
- *Chrome domes do it without the cover on*
- *The wickedest wisps in the West*
- *I'm too sexy for my hair*
  (apologies to Right Said Fred)

Chapter 8

THEY TAKE IT WORSE THAN I DO

Change in Yourself, Change for Others

If you lived all alone on a desert island and started losing your hair, you'd probably adjust to it pretty quickly. You'd have more urgent things on your mind than looking different; there would be no one to remind you of your changed appearance, no one to compare yourself with, no one to stare. But we have to work out how to live comfortably among all those loving, irritating, supportive, hostile, *others* in our lives. Because the change is physical and visible, hair loss is seen as a public event, fair game for comment.

During the initial shock reaction family and friends may not understand the change and its significance. They miss your familiar appearance, and may feel grief at the loss of the hair they admired and the pride they took in your appearance. In addition, your loved ones have to adapt to new aspects of your personality as you learn to cope with alopecia. They worry about the wider social impact: what will people say?

Alopecia areata has been compared to an unwelcome uncle who comes to stay, and upsets everyone in the family. When panic, despair or rage hit you, those close to you may become indignant or even angry with you for not shutting up and getting on with your life as though nothing had happened. It was much less challenging for them when you were at the numb stage. They may even try to convince you to ignore your feelings and the need to grieve by suggesting hair loss is trivial.

Responses may reflect fear or hostility due to ignorance, or unacknowledged fear of death or aging. The stage *they* are at in the grieving process influences how they react, for instance with hostility (anger) or refusal to talk about it (denial). But their feelings are theirs, not yours; the task for family or close friends is to get information and support and work out how to cope with their own emotions.

It is a curious fact that most of the time, people 'mirror' how you view yourself. Just as dogs attack those who are afraid, but can be won over by a show of confidence - like displaying an open hand for them to sniff - so people can sense anxiety. One response to anxiety and vulnerability is compassion, but those who are insecure - who are under stress or perhaps fear the same qualities in themselves - may react with hostility. You may be picked on because others *expect* you to be anxious about your hair loss. But if you respect yourself and expect the same from others, that's what you are most likely to receive in return. Even if you're fearful inside, you can *act* as if you're not. Try it and see if you notice the difference. A book I found excellent reading for this stage in my life was Susan Jeffer's *Feel the Fear and Do It Anyway*. Acting fearless doesn't always work with those you are closest to: they may know you too well. But a little self-confidence and assertiveness sometimes improves an unsatisfactory relationship.

It takes time for others to adjust to the new you, too. The change in you requires them to review their attitudes, behaviour, values, and may provoke uncomfortable new emotions. It's a challenge to relationships: it can tear them apart or it can deepen love, trust and understanding. John Bradshaw likens the family to a mobile - if one part is touched, the others rock until the whole finds balance once more. Friends, family and dates or partners who accept hair loss prove that their commitment is more than skin (or follicle) deep. How others handle your hair loss is a good indicator of how well they might handle other changes - illness, unemployment, death.

Silkheads and their family circle sometimes blame alopecia for the break-up of a relationship, loss of confidence, arguments with family or friends, or being unable to find a mate. Yet hair loss doesn't *cause* a marriage breakdown - people do. Hair loss can act as a magnet for unfinished business; old conflicts or criticisms that were never resolved may start flying around again. If a physical change is treated as a family tragedy or your personal nemesis, some unconnected old disappointments or frictions are probably seizing the opportunity to be voiced. Those who accuse you or your head of *making* them upset have not yet learned to 'own' their feelings.

One role many silkheads appreciate sympathizers taking on is that of explaining the medical and psychological aspects to some of the people they encounter. Having such allies lessens the burden of hair loss and normalizes it. But family members need support, because they can get so drawn into the silkhead's needs that they forget to look after their own. Everyone intimately affected by another's hair loss needs to obtain information and support, and to grieve. They need to discuss the loss and how best to handle it with people they trust. Communication can take the form of going to a support group - one specifically for families of alopecians, if possible - talking to friends and more distant relatives, medical professionals or counsellors, spiritual guides such as priest or rabbi. Those less directly affected by hair loss can help the family circle get perspective on the change.

School-age 'others' have the additional pool of teachers, school counsellor or the parents of a friend to choose from. Corresponding through newsletters is another way to explore issues and give or get advice.

The rest of the chapter looks at what effects your hair loss might have on the various categories of people you know.

Parents

A child is literally the parents' creation. Irrational as it is, parents can see alopecia, like any other illness, as their personal failure. The visibility of hair loss can make them feel that everyone knows and judges them for producing 'flawed goods.' Many ask themselves the unanswerable question, "What did we do to deserve this?" There is a sense of frustration and impotence when their child has a problem they can't alleviate. Loss and all the associated emotions are brought right into the heart of the family. Because parents hope that childhood will be a carefree,

I'M NOT SURE THIS IS THE MOST NATURAL WAY TO HELP OUR POOR LISA COME TO TERMS WITH HER HAIR LOSS

playful time, they can feel guilty that their child is afflicted while they themselves are healthy. Unprovoked suffering in young children causes particular anguish.

Whether children are still at school or have flown the nest, parents also worry about the effect alopecia will have on their child's life. Their fears may run wild until they picture the child's future as unmitigated disaster: no chance of achieving success at work, security with a partner, or a fulfilling life. If the child is at school they worry about bullies and ostracism.

Parents who do not ask for and get support in dealing with their own 'negative' feelings may turn on the child, either directly, blaming him or her, or indirectly, disagreeing or criticizing over seemingly irrelevant issues. To view hair loss as providing the motivation to explore and resolve friction is more mature than scolding the victim, for "causing all this trouble." However great their love, parents under stress may resent or be unable to provide the time and/or money to do the best for a child who needs extra medical or emotional attention.

Some parents feel rejected or angry if their child deals with hair loss differently from how they advise - just as they might over choice of job, image, boyfriend, etc.

> "It's hard enough already, just keeping on top of it. Work's difficult, I wear different hats, so they think it's my style. But my mom and I have fights all the time about my hair. She wants me to wear a wig and I don't. I try to tell her times have changed and it doesn't matter so much, but she won't listen. I'm nineteen, why can't she leave me alone? It's *my* alopecia, not hers."

Mothers are usually the primary parent with child-rearing the largest part of their role and identity, so they may feel the anguish of a child's loss of hair keenly, especially since women are judged more by their appearance than men. Women generally express their emotions more than men, so a mother's troubled feelings are more likely to show than a father's.

Mother-daughter relationships are often the closest in the family, which may lead to the mother 'adopting' the daughter's feelings of rejection and anxiety. A mother's responses could be coloured by disappointments over her own life; she may unknowingly transfer some very intense but irrelevant emotions using alopecia as the 'peg'.

When their child loses hair it is often the parents who are almost inconsolable. The child, then, not only has the burden of coping with it himself but feels responsible for the grief the alopecia causes his parents, when what he wants is to lean on them for support. This can build into resentment in older children:

"I wish they could get my alopecia into perspective. I know they care, but I mean, it's not the end of the world. It's not like a nuclear disaster or something."

In sum, parents' reactions can include anger, grief, shame, a sense of futility and powerlessness, despair, fear and guilt. But when they make time to grieve and adjust, when they treat their child with love and respect and communicate with honesty, not only do they allow their child the opportunity to adjust but they often learn valuable lessons themselves, and the relationship is enriched.

What children need is for parents to believe in them and listen to them and their emotions and wishes. They need to know that whatever happens to them, their parents trust their children can handle it, with help.

Siblings

Hair loss can be hard on young siblings who don't understand the situation. An NCCS newsletter mentions an

8-year-old talking about her older brother who had just died of cancer:

"It was a little hard to look at him sometimes because he had lost his hair."

Again, hair loss can be blamed for the bad relations between brothers and sisters that existed beforehand. Siblings of alopecians may be verbally or even physically attacked for having a 'weirdo' or 'baldy' brother or sister. Being associated with baldness can cause embarrassment, especially if they are at the stage when they depend on the approval of a peer group for self-esteem, around the ages of 8 or 9 to late teens or early twenties. If scapegoated by their peers, they may scapegoat their silkhead in turn. They may also begrudge the extra parental attention and time the 'special' one gets. But some siblings take on a protective role and display a down-to-earth view. A NAAF newsletter reports how the brother of a boy with alopecia areata views it:

"If you don't have much hair when you're born or when you die, it really doesn't matter if you don't have much in between."

Partners

(Included here are boy/girlfriends, husbands/wives and live-in partners.)

Hair loss is often an ordeal by fire, testing the strength of a relationship. In a good relationship the partner helps the silkhead through the rocky stages. Partners who prove that their love goes beyond appearances prove they can be trusted; they can probably be relied upon in sickness and in health and through life's 'slings and arrows.' Working through hair loss offers an opportunity to develop deeper trust, openness and the kind of intimacy that many cou-

143

ples do not experience till they're older, if at all.

The main problem encountered in good relationships is when the silkhead turns in on him or herself and excludes the partner. This may be an attempt to protect the partner from the upsetting emotions resulting from hair loss, or they may withdraw through fear of rejection. Committed partners declare that they understand the experience is traumatic, and that their love, attraction and desire for the silkhead remain. Although many sufferers find this hard to believe in the first shock of hair loss, it is essential to make the effort, otherwise their lack of trust and neglect may push the partner into withdrawing or even leaving. One husband comments:

> "It was a bit of a shock when her hair fell out, but I soon got used to it. Problem was, *she* didn't. All I wanted to do was help her, she was so upset. But she didn't want to talk about it and she didn't want me to touch her, for months. It was terrible being shut out like that. After a while I just gave up - I was having to work extra hours because she stopped work for a while, so that took my mind off it. I thought she might end up wanting to get divorced, not because of me but because she was so mixed up about her hair. But things began to change, slowly. It was lucky I stuck around - we got to know different sides of each other and now we're happier together than ever before."

It takes patience to allow the silkhead time to grieve and recover some sense of self. It may take longer than the partner would wish, and longer for the silkhead to recover the sense of sexuality that hair loss often damages (with cancer, sex drive may drop anyway as a result of chemotherapy). But without intercourse there are many ways of being close, affectionate and intimate to explore.

The partner may need to grieve for the loss of the familiar old partner, in order to make space for the new silkhead. Previous goals, habits, commitments may have to be pushed aside to work through new concerns; relationship counselling can clarify issues and alternatives. The partner is often best placed to give his or her family information about the condition, explaining what the silkhead is going through and reaffirming the couple's commitment to each other.

Some couples split up - divorce is not uncommon following any major life change. Often the hair loss is simply the newest weapon in an ongoing battle.

Hall of Fame

ELIZABETH STEEL gave up her career as a TV journalist when she developed alopecia areata. She went on to found British-based alopecia network Hairline International for fellow-sufferers and has written *Coping With Sudden Hair Loss.*

"He just didn't know how to cope. Here I was wondering if I was going to live or not, my world turned upside down - and all that pain... And *he* was having tantrums because I wasn't the beautiful, healthy woman he'd fallen in love with. He'd always commented on other women and their looks, but it wasn't a joke any more. I think he felt he didn't make the grade with a sick girlfriend. I blame his job, too - the music industry is so competitive and the guys are always checking out each other's status by the women they pull. I'll know to pick a man not a boy the next time round."

145

Luckily this type of ending is rare. Most partners take their cue from how the alopecian handles the problem. One older woman commented:

> "If *you* work on believing that you are still attractive and lovable, and expect him to think so too, he will usually rise to the occasion!"

Children

Children all over the world live through traumas: wars, epidemics, lack of food, loss of parents, sexual abuse. Despite such scars, many children are more resilient than adults imagine. They surprise their alopecian parent with perspective, support and unconditional love.

The hardest part for children is being kept in the dark about the hair loss and its cause: it's that old fear of the unknown. Parents need to explain the condition - and confess to being upset because of illness or feeling unattractive.

Taunts and bullying from others about their parent being a 'baldy' or wearing a wig are best handled by another adult who will listen to the child and help them work out how to deal with these problems. The silkhead and partner may be too close to the problem and have their own difficulties to work through.

Teenagers

While some teens act as lovingly as younger children, others mock parents or siblings for any unusual physical feature. Pre-existing conflict may flare into aggression as they go through the painful transition from child to adult, when their bodies are mature but they are still dependents. If they feel insecure about their identity and self-worth, and powerless - 'treated like a kid' - they may seize the parent's or sibling's hair loss as a weapon. At last, they can get back at someone!

The loss of their parent's hair may disturb them - it is a sign that parents aren't perfect and will change and age. Teenagers who don't yet know how to cope with complex emotions often express their confusion as hostility, direct or indirect.

Most teens are very dependent on peer groups; it's the developmental stage they are at. A family member's 'abnormality' could mean rejection and complete social isolation for them. Teens are scathing about age and anything that symbolizes it, so hair loss can be a symbol which embodies their worst fear. One woman with alopecia areata has a teenage son who takes it as his *own* personal tragedy that she has patchy, thin hair. He is a heavy metal fan: to him and his friends, long hair is *the* symbol of identity and therefore acceptance. His mother has had to work hard to feel good about herself in order to rise above his hurtful remarks.

Classmates

While young people sometimes suffer hell at school - insults, wigs pulled off, loneliness - others find their friends and teachers are caring. No one can predict how classmates will respond to hair loss. Where one child goes through school lonely and suffering daily abuse, another will find that he has friends galore and accepts the occasional taunt about having bald patches as no more significant than fellow-students being called "Zit face". One sixteen year-old girl, whose classmates knew she wore a wig, was voted Homecoming Queen.

In her book about children with cancer, *I Want to Grow Hair*, Erma Bombeck relates how a young child's experience of cancer was transformed by his teacher. While he was away having chemotherapy, she took time to explain all about cancer to his classmates. Just before he returned, some of the boys decided they wanted to shave off their hair too, to make him feel at home.

A good way to support a young silkhead is to talk directly to the school's principal and to other teachers or school counsellors. Children pick up hurtful attitudes from their parents, so some adult education needs to take place too. Leaflets are helpful, and some support groups send members into school to talk about the issues with staff and students. Ignorance creates needless suffering, while knowledge makes allies who deal with tormenters, so that the child can get on with work and play.

Friends

Hair loss is an excellent test of friendship: those whose warmth persists are be treasured. Joking is sometimes the only way people know of handling fear or uncomfortably mixed feelings about appearance and aging. But if friends won't stop making 'jokes' about hair, even when the alopecian has indicated this is hurtful or annoying, seeing less of them will improve self-esteem.

Alopecia is an opportunity to evaluate friends: what is likeable about them, and what their friendship offers. It *is* possible to make new friends, despite a change in appearance, and to hold out for relationships that are supportive and nourishing.

Friends can be a lifeline during times of crisis, and can provide a safe place to practise new ways of behaving. Telling a close friend about losing hair is a very important first step in adjusting. Good friends demonstrate a degree of objectivity, respect and appreciation that may be lacking in immediate family.

Work and Workmates

In spite of current ideas about freedom and equality, systematic discrimination still happens to the physically different, whether the difference is skin colour, size, disability or baldness. John T. Capps III, for example, the proud 'chrome dome' who founded the Bald Headed Men of America, was fired from his job because of his lack of hair. Judging by the success he has made of his organization, his employers lost far more than they gained.

More than one million of the five million cancer sufferers in the US "experience some form of employment discrimination solely because of their cancer history," says civil rights attorney Barbara Hoffman in an NCCS newsletter. This is partly because employers often shoulder the burden of medical insurance. In Canada and Britain, with their government-funded health care services, discrimination has more to do with irrational fears about cancer signifying disability or death. This ignores the fact that many people diagnosed with cancer survive to live productive lives. My hope is that the lobbying and legal cases brought by individuals and groups such as NCCS, NAAF and BHMA, as well as the example of some European countries, might lead to a more efficient and compassionate use of human resources.

> **Hall of Fame**
>
> CARL REINER, comedy actor and director *(Dead Men Don't Wear Plaid)*, on his lack of hair: "Anyone who wears hair during the daytime is overdressed."

Under these difficult circumstances many people find it best to keep their hair loss or cancer as secret as possible. But some find it a strain to have part of their attention on guarding their secret.

For those in image-conscious jobs such as sales, televi-

149

sion or film, hair loss brings the added strain of expensive wigs or surgical procedures and the constant worry of exposure. Some leave such jobs in favour of a field where what they do is more important than how they look. A rapidly balding marketing representative is now re-training in paralegal work:

"I figured if I'd stayed a few more years I'd have had youngsters being promoted over me anyway, just because I'd *look* older. I'm glad I decided to bail out when I did - this way I'm getting back into the job market before I reach that post-40s unemployable stage."

Those who work in supportive, open-minded organizations sometimes change the status quo to fit them, through educating workmates.

"I use my alopecia (totalis) as a public awareness tool. When I walk into a place I mention it right away. I say something like, 'I look a little different from most men, but what I've got isn't contagious or damaging.' Then I explain about alopecia. Using my hair loss for educational purposes is my way of adjusting. I don't find it hurts business, in fact it means the meeting starts on a more sincere, personal level - it's an approach that stands out from the traditional sales pitch."

Not all jobs are amenable to openness, however. Silkheads have to be quick-thinking and make their own judgements about whom it's safe to tell.

"I've worked in the store for years and nobody knows this hair isn't mine. Recently a customer told one guy that she really liked my wig. He came over to tell me the joke - and wondered why I didn't laugh. I felt really awkward, but told him, 'She's very perceptive.' He was so shocked he walked away without saying anything. But later he came back and said he wouldn't tell any of the other guys because they can be cruel about how women look."

As a self-employed computer consultant I wore a beret at preliminary discussions, if we met in person; I told clients about my alopecia after they hired me. I was either treated as normal or received extra appreciation for providing good service in spite of my 'handicap.' For journalism interviews I sometimes wear a wig; other times I go bald and joke about "keeping a cool head under pressure."

Strangers

To trust, or not to trust? People have got a bad press - literally. Every day we hear about murderers, rapists, muggers, child molesters, as if that's what all people are like. Hair loss is hard to cope with when we expect the worst from others. But for every 'attacker' there are thousands of others who are indifferent (they have their own lives to worry about), mildly curious or caring. And it's not until we are ready to risk, to trust others that we find out just how wonderful strangers can be.

Naturally, generalizations don't hold all the time, everywhere. I thought it was easier to go bald publicly because I worked in a city where I felt anonymous; there were already all sorts of eccentrics. Yet a woman from a village in rural Wales said,

"I could never have stopped wearing my wig in a city. All those people! I've lived in this village for over twenty years so it didn't seem too threatening. It was much easier than I expected - most people didn't turn a hair."

There are variations from culture to culture, too. People in England tend to be more reserved, and either ignore

151

Love Needs Hair Like A Fish Needs A Bicycle
(*or* Dread Of Dating)

• Will she notice?

• How can I tell him?

• She'd freak out if she knew I have no pubic hair.

Dating experiences can be moving, sad, or hilarious (with hindsight) - sometimes a combination of all three. Yet many silkheads have excellent romantic and sexual relationships. Communication is at the heart of closeness, so this is the area to concentrate on.

When you long to be special to someone, embarrassment and shame at baldness can be acute. Although not telling avoids embarrassment, it makes trust difficult. Serious misconceptions can arise: unusual behaviour, such as avoiding being caressed in the neck and hair region, may be interpreted as lack of interest. The bald patches or wig may be taken as a sign of an unmentionable, devastating illness such as AIDS.

So how do people 'confess'?

• "I've got a rare body. It's particularly smooth..."

• "Hair is a strange thing. Believe it or not, some people lose all of theirs. I'm one."

• get drunk and let things slip

• get so angry that you pull your wig off

• roleplay a natural way to bring up hair loss, e.g. when you see a bald actor or athlete in an ad or TV program.

• ask a good friend to tell your date

• arrange so your lover sees you when you are asleep - without your wig

Sharing how you feel about hair loss increases and encourages intimacy. And if you're unlucky enough to be dating someone who is put off by your condition, just remind yourself:

*"Any man or woman who doesn't want **me** is just not worth it."*

silkheads or look away in embarrassment. Other Europeans tend to stare more openly. Women in a primitive Turkish village, every inch of their bodies apart from face covered in black cloth, screamed and waved their arms at the sight of me. North Americans sometimes ask me directly, "Why have you shaved your head?" I like this: I can tell them about alopecia and dispel some of the ignorance that lies at the root of much of the anguish over hair loss. Responding to repeated curiosity, a standard response from strangers, requires patience, particularly when you are leading as busy a life as anyone with hair.

People often confess they thought I had cancer; they will tell me about some loss they have suffered, or about a family member with alopecia areata. It's almost as though we need an excuse to open up and have human contact with each other and talk about the things that really matter in our lives; hair loss can provide such an opening.

Those who wear wigs also experience the kindness of strangers:

> "It was in a gale - my wig had already blown off once. The second time I just stood there for a couple of seconds in a panic - and this man, a complete stranger, suddenly took off his jacket and popped it over my head, then went and got my wig for me. I went to the nearest washroom for repairs. When I came out and gave him back his jacket he said he wore a hairpiece himself. What a gentleman!"

When people stare or gossip or call insults, it wounds our already damaged dignity and pride. Yet the insulters are almost always cowards who need the protection of a group. Sometimes they are men who take the liberty to comment on any stranger's appearance. Usually it is a group of young men. If the situation isn't threatening a 'Snappy Answer' can discharge the tension, as can explaining to them about hair loss - they are obviously interested! This destroys the 'victim' image. To walk away and ignore hostility is also powerful, though it may not feel so inside. Whichever way confrontation is dealt with on the spot, it's important to process an attack afterwards by telling someone, having a cry or simply thinking of all the clever retorts that could have been made.

Chapter 9

STRAW INTO GOLD

Hair loss itself is never something positive - it's what people do with it that counts. It's an important distinction. Some claim loss has made them into better people, but hair loss itself doesn't *make* anyone into something else. *We* do the good work, through the way we respond to it, and we deserve to give ourselves full credit, praise and gratitude for the miracles we effect. The positive aspect of hair loss is, simply, learning to acknowledge all those wonderful aspects of ourselves. It reminds me of the tale of Rumpelstiltskin: we learn the magical, transferable skill of spinning straw into gold, loss into gain.

Hair loss can act as a catalyst to draw out qualities of maturity such as self-acceptance and compassion for others. It can force us to stop racing around in an overstressed world and coast into a period of reflection. We discover more about the 'real' us, and about what we value in life. We can affect the lives of others in ways that are deeply rewarding, both to them and to ourselves. We learn the value of trust. There's a whole rethinking of values and attitudes from which we make new decisions and take new actions.

Personal Liberation

When I stopped covering my head I realized that my appearance suggested I was avant-garde, unique, image-conscious yet ascetic, daring, fantastic... Although at the time I felt more like something unpleasant found under a rock, I learned to explore, to 'try on' these qualities. I could use my hair loss rather than fight it.

After going through a very competitive education system I spent years haunted with doubt about my own worth. Only the loss of my hair helped me to stop comparing myself with others, usually to my detriment. Now I am learning to accept I am me, completely individual and valuable in myself - no matter what anyone else does or thinks. My confidence has risen dramatically. This is a common lesson, as a secretary confirms:

> "I almost killed myself when big patches of my hair disappeared, but now I think it was a blessing in disguise. At last I was convinced that my boyfriend really loved *me*, not just how I looked. It was like snorkelling - suddenly I saw a whole world existed underneath the surface."

The terrifying experience of being 'alone in the wilderness' is something few people choose. Yet most religious leaders have sought out just this: Jesus with his forty days in the desert, Mohammed similarly, Moses' forty years in the desert and Buddha's lengthy retreat under the Bodhi tree. For them, the period in the wilderness gave birth to insight, enlightenment and spiritual strengthening, and so it is for many who lose hair.

Liberating Others

Admitting that you have lost your hair signals to others that they can open up about their losses or sorrows, rather than having to hide these aspects of their lives.

Your handling of a major problem can help others to find their true selves: you become a role-model without even realizing it. For example, after seeing me just one evening, at a dinner party, a physician I had never met before suddenly came out as gay, for the first time in his life. A store owner relates:

"I started losing my hair when I was twenty five, and by thirty it was mostly gone, but I wasn't worried. You see, I had already joined a particular spiritual group whose leader was bald - or almost - and so I thought baldness was a wonderful thing. I was happy to become more like the man I so admired."

And simply talking with those who share the same problem can literally change their lives. A young store clerk said:

"Most weeks I see at least a few people in the mall who are either wearing a wig or have some kind of hair loss. I always go up to them and mention that I have it. We get talking, and sometimes we go and sit and have a coffee and talk for ages. Some people start crying, and I generally follow! But they are always so relieved to talk with someone who knows."

Going public with hair loss can transform awareness on a large scale. The idea that TV viewers have to be protected from 'unacceptable' looks is contradicted by the experience of Rick Smith, ex-presenter of nationally-networked *PM Magazine*. After developing extensive alopecia areata, he wore a hairpiece before the camera but never felt quite right about it. In an interview in the *Boston Globe,* he explained:

"It wasn't me. I wanted to complete the healing, accept the loss. I wanted to show that I was OK, happy, healthy, fine, and that there was no reason to hide."

One historic day he decided to take off his hairpiece in front of the camera and present his real, patchy head to his viewers. He found them extremely supportive.

"I got calls and letters saying it was about time there was something real on television."

When he is not working as Executive Director of Rhode Is-

land Film Commission, Smith educates the public about alopecia, and broadcasts his message is that far from being ridi-
culed or rejected, we silkheads can be inspirational heroes
ourselves.

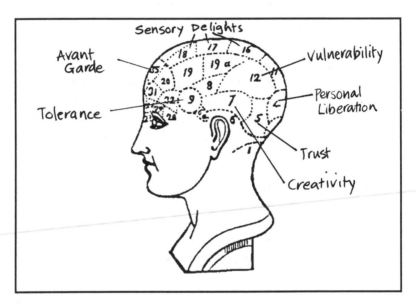

Vulnerability

We spend the first half of our life building up defences to
establish our personal boundaries and protect ourselves from
emotional hurt. The set of habits and behaviours that develop
- such as not getting too close to colleagues, or falling into a
routine with your partner - are called the *persona*.

Hair loss breaches a hole in our defences and leaves us
more open to hurt, which can be scary. Why then take a step
backward towards being more vulnerable, instead of plug-
ging the hole? Having a strong protective persona can gradually make us set in our ways, creatures of habit, distant from
others and even rather bored. Having fewer defences allows

us to shed some of that adult stiffness. We can dare to take risks, dare to trust, to be open and more spontaneous. The pay-offs are worth it for me, giving me renewed optimism, and mental exhilaration as well. Although I hated feeling vulnerable at the time, I now appreciate the opportunity alopecia handed me.

Tolerance

All of us who lose hair encourage tolerance of those who look different, by our very existence. We may not want to - it's uncomfortable to encounter prejudice - but here we are. We offer the chance to those we tell about our hair loss, to grow in compassion and understanding.

For me one of the most important gains was tolerance. Before The Fall I thought I was unprejudiced and accepting. It took meeting other sufferers to show me that there are almost as many ways of dealing with hair loss as there are silkheads. Instead of thinking of us all as damaged clones, I started to appreciate the individual beneath the hair loss. One woman with female pattern baldness said:

"I thank God for my hair loss every day. It reminds me of deeper values and that what really counts in this world is not what we look like but who we are. I know how lucky I am in the midst of so much suffering to have such a small problem."

Besides the invisible gains we spin from our lost strands, there are the practical advantages.

Sensory Delights

A whole new world of sensation opens up: our scalps are among our most sensitive parts. Discovering head sensations can lead into re-discovering other sensational experiences. So often the sense of touch is forgotten in a world where the eyes, ears and taste-buds get the most attention.

159

- Taking a shower gives the most wonderful massage
- Air, sunshine, even rain on one's head gives a new slant on going 'straight to the head': it's an instant lift to the mind
- A cat or dog, or a loved one, snuggling up to your clean pate can be a real thrill
- Losing hair exposes a whole new area for your imagination and your lover's to use in love-making

Wigs - the 'New, Improved' Hair

Silkheads can look better than Before The Fall, and can

Save Time, Money and Energy!

- men may be able to stop shaving
- women who used to shave body hair save all that time and hassle
- little or no hair to look after frees time and attention for activities, relationships, new experiences, volunteer work...
- no hair means no anguish at going grey or attempts to hide it

No hairpiece?

- save money, time and anxiety: no need to wash, condition or style
- no money on hairdressers, hairdryers, mousses, combs & all the paraphernalia
- no tangles or lengthy drying times
- an evening in a club or bar leaves stale smoke only on clothes, not on hair
- no dandruff; dry or itchy scalp easier to treat without hair

Hairpiece?

- save time because styling stays much longer
- save money: infrequent 'maintenance' sessions at hairdressers

choose any type of 'hair'. You can change your appearance in an instant, and adopt a more playful attitude to image than most people can.

At a NAAF conference one of the delegates was being ignored by the hotel staff, who were busy attending to older businessmen, answering telephones and chatting with each other. This silkhead suddenly leaned over the counter and pushed her wig a few inches up her head - and received instant attention.

A story for which I have been unable to track the source - perhaps it is one of those urban myths - is of a cancer patient in New York. One evening she was approached by a mugger, and in a moment of inspiration pulled off her wig. The would-be attacker was so shocked by this aggressive act that he fled.

Creativity

Forget 'paint your wagon' - you have your own walking canvas. While it may not be appropriate to walk around decorated in everyday life, bare spots or scalp are perfect for fancy dress parties or charity events. Greasepaint or ordinary make-up rubs off easily; for long-lasting artwork use water-based theatrical make-up (available from fancy dress or theatrical goods stores). Asking family or friends to put designs on your head is a great way for them to experience another side of the tragedy of hair loss.

Take photos of your head. Pose for artists, many of whom have never had the chance to draw what the head actually looks like, from life.

The Right Head in the Right Place

Many silkheads avoid swimming altogether, or feel they have to 'cover up' in the water. Yet professional swimmers often shave their heads, and even their bodies, for better performance. Your fellow swimmers are more likely to wonder what event you're training for than what's wrong with you. Body-builders and some other sports enthusiasts (e.g. basketball players) also often shave their heads and/or bodies because it looks good, it looks athletic - and it's one less distraction from their performance.

If you have little or none of that dangerous, unsanitary stuff called hair, there's no need to wear those horrible caps to work in factories, commercial kitchens or around farm machinery. And little chance of suffering the fate of Keats' Porphyria, who was strangled with her own hair.

Being conspicuous can have its own rewards for the adventurous:

> "When I walked into this club some wise guy called me 'Paul Shaeffer' - that's the almost bald band leader on David Letterman's show. Instead of getting upset, I went along with it and pretended I really *was* him. People bought me drinks, I signed autographs, I had a great night out!"

The Bald Headed Men of America annual conference gives members the chance to have their heads voted sexiest, most beautiful, most kissable... What thickly haired men ever get that sort of opportunity?

Happy endings don't exist: none of us have got to the end yet. They aren't what count anyway. Living life courageously and lovingly transforms tragedy into a source of strength, vitality, and inspiration.

Useful Organizations

National Coalition for Cancer Survivorship
1010 Wayne Avenue, Suite 300
Silver Spring
MD 20910
U.S.A.

American Cancer Society
1599 Clifton Road N.E.
Atlanta
GA 30329
U.S.A.

Canadian Cancer Society
1702 - 77 Bloor Street W.
Toronto
Ontario
Canada M5S 3A1

Hairline International
39 St. John's Close
Knoll
Solihull
West Midlands
England B93 0NN

Bald Headed Men of America
3819 Bridges Street
Morehead City
NC 28557
U.S.A.

Canadian Alopecia Areata Association
c/o Hazel Anaka
Box 382
Andrew
Alberta
Canada T0B 0C0

National Alopecia Areata Foundation
P.O. Box 150760
CA 94915-0760
U.S.A.

BIBLIOGRAPHY
This is not a complete bibliography but it does include a sample of the books and articles I found most useful. Consult a librarian for guidance among the hundreds of articles in medical journals.

Aldhizer, Gerard & Krop, Thomas
The Doctors' Book on Hair Loss Prentice-Hall, New York, 1983
Benson, Herbert and Proctor, William
Beyond the Relaxation Response Berkley, New York, 1985
Berman, Morris
The Reenchantment of the World Cornell University Press, N. Y., 1984
Bombeck, Erma
I Want To Grow Hair Harper & Row, New York, 1989
Brohn, Penny
The Bristol Programme Century Hutchinson, London, 1987
Bruning, Nancy
Coping with Chemotherapy Doubleday, New York, 1985
Cameron, Ann
A Whole Brass Band Harbour Publishing, BC, Canada 1992
Cooper, Wendy
Hair Aldus, London, 1971
Corson, Richard
Fashions in Hair Peter Owen, London, 1965
Cousins, Norman
Head First Penguin, New York, 1989
Dawber, Rodney and Rook, Arthur
Diseases of the Hair and Scalp Blackwell, Oxford (UK), 1982
Van Deusen, Edmund
What You Can Do About Baldness Stein & Day, New York, 1978
Dolan, John P. and Adams-Smith, William N.
Health and Society Seabury Press, New York, 1978
Goffman, Erving
Stigma Simon and Schuster, New York, 1963
Inglis, Brian
The Diseases of Civilisation Granada, UK
Inglis, Brian and West, Ruth
The Alternative Health Guide Michael Joseph, London, 1983
Kubler-Ross, Elisabeth
On Death and Dying Macmillan, New York, 1969
National Alopecia Areata Foundation
Mental Health Handbook

National Coalition of Cancer Survivorship
Teamwork: The Cancer Patient's Guide
Nesbit, E.
Melisande Walker Books, London, 1989
Pervan, Anthony
Natural Hair Growth F. Fell, Florida, 1987
Ridington, Gill
Who Do We Think We Are? Disabled Women's Network, Canada 1989
Sandomir, Richard
The Incredible Adventures of Baldman Macmillan, New York, 1991
Sontag, Susan
Illness as Metaphor; AIDS and Its Metaphors Doubleday, N. Y., 1989
Steel, Elizabeth
Coping with Sudden Hair Loss Thorsons (UK) 1988
Stoll, Basil (ed)
Coping with Cancer Dordrecht, Boston, 1987
US Dept of Health and Human Services
Young People with Cancer: A Handbook for Parents 1982
Wolf, Naomi
The Beauty Myth Chatto and Windus, London, 1991
Woodforde, John
The Strange Story of False Hair Routledge & Kegan Paul, London, 1971
Wylie, Betty
New Beginnings Key Porter, Toronto, 1991

ARTICLES

Barber, Anne **The Psyche-Soma Connection**
Somatics Journal
Baxley, K.O. et al. **Alopecia: Effect on Cancer Patients' Body Image**
Cancer Nursing 7(6): 499-503, Dec 1984
Beard, H.O. **Social and Psychological Implications of Alopecia Areata**
Journal of the American Academy of Dermatology 14(4): 697-700 Apr 86
Consumer Reports **Baldness: Is There Hope?**
Consumer Reports 53(9): 543-547 Sep 1988
Dawber, R. **Aetiology and Pathophysiology of Hair Loss**
Dermatologica 175 (Supp. 2): 23-28 1987
Gosselin, C. **Hair Loss, Personality and Attitudes**
Personality & Individual Differences 5(3):365-369 1984
Hordinsky, M. **General Evaluation of the Patient with Alopecia**
Dermatologic Clinics 5(3) 553-564 Jul 1987
Lyketsos et al. **Hostile Personality Characteristics**
Psychotherapy & Psychosomatics 44(3): 122-131 1985